A SHORT HISTORY OF SCIENCE

The following chapters were originally delivered as a series of Broadcast Talks to Sixth Forms during 1949–50 and were later repeated in the Third Programme. The publishers wish to thank the B.B.C. for their courtesy in facilitating the publication of this book and for permission to use part of the material contained in a pamphlet produced by them in connection with the Talks. They are also much indebted to Dr. J. Lindsay, of Girton College, Cambridge, who assisted in the preparation of the pamphlet and whose Introduction to it is here reproduced. Each author has been free to revise his Talk for publication, but the original spoken version has for the most part been retained with only slight variation.

The publishers are also indebted to the following for permission to reproduce illustrations: To Allen & Unwin Ltd. for Boyle's Second Air-Pump from *A History of Science, Technology and Philosophy, Sixteenth and Seventeenth Centuries*, by A. Wolf; to G. Bell & Sons Ltd. for The Blood System according to Galen and The Blood System according to Harvey from *The Discovery of the Circulation of the Blood*, by Charles Singer and also to the Clarendon Press for the same two illustrations from *A History of Medicine*, by Charles Singer; to William Heinemann Ltd. for the Aristotelian Scheme of the Universe from *Science, Past and Present*, by F. Sherwood Taylor.

A SHORT HISTORY
OF SCIENCE

Origins and Results of
the Scientific Revolution

A SYMPOSIUM

Doubleday Anchor Books
Doubleday & Company, Inc.
Garden City, New York
1959

COVER BY WALTER ALLNER
TYPOGRAPHY BY EDWARD GOREY

CONTENTS

INTRODUCTION

W HAT is the History of Science? The phrase as
used here means an attempt to find out what
questions man has asked at various times about the physical
universe and what answers he has found satisfying. The
Greeks, for instance, asked what was the substance of which
the whole universe was made. Some medieval thinkers
asked whether it was worth while studying cause and effect
as observed in the world of nature or whether everything
was simply to be explained as being the will of God. In the
seventeenth century men asked if the universe could not be
reduced to mathematical terms.

At certain times men were fascinated by more particular
problems within the general philosophic framework of these
larger questions. For example, towards the end of the Middle Ages, that is in the fourteenth and fifteenth centuries,
some critics of the then accepted Aristotelian system became specially interested in the problems of movement—
why did a projectile continue to move after it had left the
bow or sling and why did it gradually fall to the ground?
Aristotle's explanations were no longer accepted as satisfactory, and the way was opened for a whole new philosophy to creep into men's minds through the small hole
made in the accepted theory of motion.

In the sixteenth century some mathematicians came to
criticise the generally accepted theories about the position
and motion of the heavenly bodies. Copernicus was one of
those who found the usual explanations clumsy. This was
partly because he was in search of a neater mathematical
solution. But he was also influenced by the Renaissance
ideas which had made a Platonic rather than an Aristotelian

philosophy fashionable, and therefore tried to find an ideal perfection expressing itself throughout the universe.

In the seventeenth century such thinkers as Galileo, Kepler and Newton tried to find mathematical laws which would explain the movements of all bodies, both in heaven and on earth.

In the eighteenth century some men occupied themselves with the nature of gases and tried to discover what were the component elements of matter; others asked what was the nature and what were the properties of the mysterious force called electricity. In the nineteenth century men were asking new questions and finding new answers in every branch of science. Two of these answers which had immediate repercussions—one in the realm of belief and one in that of public health—were the theory of evolution and the theory of infection.

The History of Science is also partly a study of problems of practical technique; how men managed to capture gases, or measure the amount of blood pumped through the heart in an hour. It therefore involves some study of scientific instruments and of the technique of scientific experiment. It also involves a study of the interaction of scientific ideas with the other ideas commonly held at the time and expressed, for example, in poems and plays. It is a study of what ordinary educated men thought about the universe and themselves at any particular time, and so it is part of the general history of civilisation.

One remarkable problem that emerges from the study of the History of Science is why so many advances were achieved quite apart from any improvement in instruments or the collection of new facts. Thinkers looked at familiar material, but saw a new significance which had not been perceived before. Copernicus, for example, did not experiment and observed very little. He chiefly considered material which had been collected and examined by earlier scholars. The application of a new mind to familiar material produced a new result. Another problem is the extent to which scientific development took place to meet social and economic needs, and how far the developments took place because of the internal developments within science itself or because of the genius of some particular scientist.

For the historian the History of Science poses special problems. If the growth of scientific thought is seen as an essential part of the development of modern civilisation, then various historical events assume a rather different position in the new perspective. The Renaissance, as Professor Butterfield observes, can appear as 'one of the most typically medieval things that the Middle Ages ever produced' (that is to say, the last of a series of revivals of interest in classical antiquity) and the Reformation can become 'a minor dispute within the fold of western Christendom'. The 'Scientific Revolution', which culminated in the seventeenth century, is seen as the beginning of the modern age and of more importance than any other historical event since the spread of Christianity.

The sixteen chapters of this book are not intended to form a comprehensive history of science, but they offer samples of the different problems which present themselves to the historian of science. Four attempt comprehensive surveys of men's ideas about the universe at four different times—before the Scientific Revolution, after Newton's discoveries, after Darwin's publication of *The Origin of Species*, and today. Three discuss science in the light of the social and economic conditions in the Middle Ages, the seventeenth century, and the early nineteenth century respectively. The rest are devoted to particular problems, and show why these problems attracted attention when they did and how they were solved.

The work of Galileo influenced so many different fields that he is treated in several of the chapters rather than being made the sole topic of one of them.

JEAN LINDSAY.

CHRONOLOGICAL TABLE

This table gives the dates of some of the persons mentioned in the book who have made an important contribution to science.

b.c. 460 B.C.	Democritus of Abdera
384–322 B.C.	Aristotle
fl. 270 B.C.	Aristarchus of Samos
A.D. 130–200	Galen of Pergamum
fl. 139	Ptolemy of Alexandria
c. 1206–1280	Albertus Magnus
1214–1292	Roger Bacon
1226–1274	Thomas Aquinas
1265–1321	Dante Alighieri
1330–1382	Nicholas Oresme
d. about 1358	Jean Buridan
1473–1543	Copernicus
1494–1555	Georg Bauer (Agricola)
1514–1564	Andreas Vesalius
1516–1559	Colombus of Padua
1519–1603	Andrea Cesalpino
1537–1619	Hieronymus Fabricius
1540–1603	William Gilbert
1546–1601	Tycho Brahe
1547–1600	Giordano Bruno
1561–1626	Francis Bacon
1564–1642	Galileo Galilei
1571–1630	Johannes Kepler
1578–1657	William Harvey
1596–1650	René Descartes
1602–1686	Otto von Guericke
1627–1691	Robert Boyle
1628–1694	Marcello Malpighi
1628–1704	John Ray
1629–1695	Christian Huygens

A SHORT HISTORY OF SCIENCE

I

DANTE'S VIEW OF
THE UNIVERSE

Herbert Butterfield

*Professor of Modern History
in the University of Cambridge*

T HE greatest obstacle to the understanding of the history of science is our inability to unload our minds
of modern views about the nature of the universe. We look
back a few centuries and we see men with brains much
more powerful than ours—men who stand out as giants in
the intellectual history of the world—and sometimes they
look foolish if we only superficially observe them, for they
were unaware of some of the most elementary scientific
principles that we nowadays learn at school. It is easy to
forget that sometimes it took centuries to discover which
end of the stick to pick up when starting on a certain kind
of scientific problem. It took ages of bitter controversy and
required the co-operative endeavour of many pioneer minds
to settle certain simple and fundamental principles which
now even children understand without any difficulty at all.

These points are remarkably illustrated in the case of the
medieval poet and thinker, Dante. It will be useful to examine Dante's view of the universe, not because he invented
that view, but because he is undoubtedly one of the greatest minds in history, and in his works he gives us a picture
of the kind of thing which was believed by the best intel-
lects of his time—that is to say, round about the year 1300.
It is important to note that in the age of Dante men were
not aware of a principle which almost comes as second

nature to us. They did not understand that all bodies have weight, and that if some of them move up rather than down that is because they are like the piece of wood which rises from the bottom of a tub of water, only moving upwards because they are less heavy than the medium in which they are immersed. In the age of Dante it was believed that some bodies had a kind of gravity which made them tend to fall, while other bodies were endowed with the opposite principle, an actual levity, a positive tendency to move upwards. Further than this, men in those days had no idea of what we should mean by a chemical element —but neither did the great founders of modern science four hundred years later, in the age of Sir Isaac Newton. It took a long controversy even in the latter part of the eighteenth century to establish the fact that water is not an element, and that in reality it represents a compound of two substances. Yet, however able men might be, it was very difficult for them to advance very far in chemistry until they had discovered which substances were primary ones.

If we take, then, first of all, the purely mundane realm, the sublunary sphere, the region this side of the moon, we see that scholars in the age of Dante believed in the existence of only four elements, four primary substances in this part of the universe. These were earth, water, air and fire, and out of a mixture of them the various substances seen on this globe were held to be composed. Earth and water were supposed to be pulled down by a principle of gravity, but air and fire were exactly the reverse—they tended to rise because they possessed the principle of levity. The air, however, was liable to have earthy particles and dusty impurities mixed with it, so that it never rose very far—it tended to cling near to the ground. Even gravity was not regarded as we should regard it—it was not thought that the earth drew the apple downwards; rather it was assumed that there was something inside the apple which made it aspire to rush down to the ground.

The men of learning in the age of Dante knew that the world was a globe, and when they made their ideal picture or pattern of the way in which the elements were arranged they imagined that the central thing, the hard core of the whole universe, was a solid globe of earth, the element of earth being heavier than the others and therefore at the bottom. Then they imagined this hard, earthy globe entirely covered with a glassy ocean, so that an encircling sphere of water entirely enwrapped the original sphere of earth. Next came the air, the atmosphere. It clung over the globe like a cap that fitted all round, so that it formed another sphere. And finally, outside all that, there was a sphere of fire, because, of course, fire always tended to rise

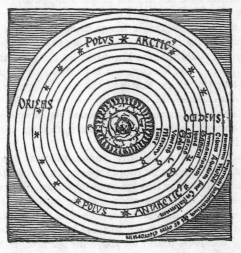

THE ARISTOTELIAN SCHEME OF THE UNIVERSE

and to push itself to the top, so that it formed another circle round the rest. That would be the kind of world that would exist, they said in those days, supposing all the elements were in their proper place, all collected into their appropriate spheres. Only, it would be a dead world, because neither the earth nor the water, neither the air nor the fire, would have any need to move from one place to another. They would never need to aspire to move in any direction, because, being in their proper spheres already, they would be at home and could simply rest.

Motion in a straight line only occurred because as a matter of fact, in the real world, the various elements were often displaced, so that they were outside their proper spheres. If we take, then, not the mere pattern of the arrangement of the elements, not the mere idealised picture of the world, but the world of real life, the men of the age of Dante believed that the various elements—the four primary substances—were mixed and entangled with one another, forming the various kinds of materials that we actually see and handle. That meant that always some of the elements were out of their proper spheres, and it made a lively world and a chancy one, with lots of motion in it, and a tendency for visible things to decay as they disintegrated into their various parts. In the case of some substances you could squeeze the water out of them, and the water, when it was released, would tend to look for its true home—tend to trickle down to the sea. Substances contained the element of fire imprisoned within them, and when they were burned this fire found its escape; it fluttered upwards, seeking its true sphere, seeking the place where it could be at rest.

There was one particularly paradoxical case where an element came outside its proper sphere. In certain regions the land had been pulled up from its proper place at the bottom—raised above the surface of the waters by special means—to form a habitation for men. Dante believed that this was only the case in the northern hemisphere and that the land had been pulled up above the sea level by an influence from the fixed stars. The land so elevated stretched from Gibraltar to the Ganges and from the Equator in the south to the Arctic Circle in the north. And in the very centre of this habitable world was Jerusalem, the Holy City. There were travellers who said that they had seen land in Africa further south than this theory implied. But Dante was a typical rationalist when he came across something that conflicted with the science that he knew. He wondered whether travellers always told the truth.

You have to remember that in the age of Dante, round about the year A.D. 1300, Western Europe was still slowly recapturing the science and the learning of antiquity—still climbing painfully back to a recovery of the high civilisa-

tion which had existed in the Graeco-Roman world, and
which still existed in New Testament days, though much
of it was lost and submerged for centuries after successive
barbarian invasions had brought about the collapse of the
Roman Empire. The views of Dante concerning the physical universe are really the views of the ancient world, and
particularly the views of Aristotle, whom he regarded as
the great master of knowledge and philosophy. Indeed, the
sway which Sir Isaac Newton held over the mind of scientists in modern centuries is nothing to be compared with the
dominion held by Aristotle in various fields of science for
two thousand years—practically down to the time of Sir
Isaac Newton himself. And, except in very minor details,
Dante's view of the universe prevailed even into the modern
centuries—it is the one which existed almost to the beginning of the seventeenth century.

If the first half of this series of discussions is largely concerned with the scientific revolution which brought about
the origin of the modern form of science and the modern
view of the universe—a revolution which largely took place
in the seventeenth century—we have to remember that this
revolution overthrew the main ideas which had been held
by the ancient world, and which had persisted through the
Middle Ages, and even in the centuries after the Italian
Renaissance. In reality, the whole campaign from the time
of Copernicus to that of Newton was conducted against
the ideas of Aristotle, and against the kind of diagram
which he had made of the universe. What we are examining
now, therefore, is the system and the view of the universe
which the scientific revolution replaces. What we shall be
studying later is the overthrow of the medieval science and
the ancient Greek science all at once. In Dante we discover
the principal things that modern science had to unlearn.

This is particularly the case when we leave the purely
mundane realm, the sublunary sphere, and examine Dante's
picture of the whole cosmos, his idea of the architecture
of the skies and the workings of the heavenly bodies. In
those days they could not imagine an infinite sky, with the
stars and planets drifting in empty space—they could never
conceive of the way in which the heavenly bodies could be

kept in their proper places under such a system. Also they could not believe that bodies might exert a 'pull' on one another across empty space, could not imagine anything like Newton's theory of attraction. They had learned from Aristotle to believe that bodies could not affect one another except by actual contact. They imagined that all the stars and planets must therefore be attached to something. Men could only see the shine of the star or the planet, but it is true today that on a dark night one may be able to see only the red lamp in the rear of a bicycle. And just as we know that the lamp must be attached to a bicycle—not sailing away on its own account—so the men of Dante's time held the view that the stars and planets must be attached to something else, though it certainly was not possible to see what this might be. It was imagined that they were fastened on to crystalline globes—a whole succession of them—which surrounded the globe of the earth and formed a series of skies.

Dante's picture of the skies consisted of a whole series of globes or spheres, one inside the other, therefore, with the hard earth at the centre of the whole system. These globes or spheres formed a successive series of heavens, but it was necessary that they should be transparent, and in point of fact, as I have said, they were recognised to be invisible. All you could see was the star or planet attached to these glassy globes or spheres, and Dante said that the planet was like a jewel riding on the back of the sphere, though some people had different theories about this. In the sixteenth century we meet with the view that the planet was like a thickening of the material of the sphere itself, or like a knot in a piece of wood, which caught the light of the sun.

Originally these spheres had been very subtle in character—almost like an ethereal fluid, moving very easily, completely frictionless and without weight. In the course of time, however, the conception hardened and it came to be assumed that they were rather glassy crystalline spheres, transparent but impenetrable. Indeed, there was a further sense in which the scientific views of the age of Dante showed a radical difference from anything that we have seen in recent centuries. Though the earth itself was thought to be composed of four elements as we have seen, everything in the skies—the spheres and the heavenly bodies —was considered to consist of a different kind of matter, a fifth essence, a peculiarly perfect kind of material. While everything on the earth was subject to change and decay, the material that formed the skies was unchanging and incorruptible. Also it was in its proper sphere already—it had no need to aspire to go up or down. It had neither weight nor levity—it could only move like a circle which turns while for ever remaining in the same place. For this reason all the motions that took place in the sky, even the irregular motions of the planets, had always to be reduced to a form of circular motion.

According to Dante there were ten of the spheres or skies which I have described—the one nearest to the earth carried the moon, the third had Venus attached to it, while the eighth one had all the fixed stars scattered over it, and revolved with them round our globe. The last sphere of all, the tenth, was the Empyrean Heaven; but the ninth was a very interesting one, because though there was no visible sign of its existence it was argued that logically its existence was necessary. It was called the Primum Mobile and it had the function of turning all the skies together round the motionless earth every twenty-four hours to produce the alternation of night and day. As it was one of the outside spheres, this meant that it had to move very quickly, and it was thought that it had good reason for this ardour and eagerness—it was next to the Empyrean Heaven. Since the days when Aristotle had given currency to this whole system or pattern of the skies, astronomical observation had led to many corrections and complications. It was found necessary to add to the intricacy of the machinery, because it was clear to the observer that the planets did not move in regular circles—as seen from the earth, some of them alter their speed, pursue an irregular course, seem at times to stop in the sky, and even appear to go backwards. So new spheres had to be added to complicate the movement, rather like cog wheels in a piece of clockwork. The planet Venus, for example, rode round on the back of one sphere and, while it was moving, that sphere itself was riding on the back of another sphere. By the opening of modern times it was necessary to have over eighty of these spheres, forming the machinery of the heavens. Observations, however, were remarkably accurate, and men had been accumulating them for centuries; so that even on this curious astronomical system it proved possible to make accurate predictions of the places where planets would be at some future date. In Dante's *Divine Comedy* there is a passage which shows him to be aware that the existing calendar was wrong by one day in a hundred years—a point which was remedied in the sixteenth century by dropping the leap year once every hundred years.

It will be seen that not only the fundamental principles but the whole diagram or picture of the universe was utterly different from that of modern science. The difference ran throughout the whole system, and on Dante's view gravity could only apply to the earth and the things of the earth. If you carried a stone near to a distant planet it would fall not on to that planet, but back to the earth, because the heavenly bodies knew nothing of gravitation. All ordinary matter aspired to reach the centre of the earth, because this was also the centre of the universe itself. The consequences of this fundamental difference ran throughout the whole of men's thinking and altered their attitude to many things. In modern times we think that the moon is romantic, but in Dante it is rather drab, it is too low in the skies, too near to mundane things. It is the sun that makes Dante romantic—though, of course, the sun moves round the motionless earth, and he does not see it as the centre of anything like a solar system. One of the greatest differences between Dante and the modern world—one of the greatest hurdles that men had to get over before modern science could find its feet—lay in the problem of motion. We today have what is called a principle of inertia in accordance with which we imagine that if a body is once in motion it will continue that motion in a straight line unless something intervenes to stop it, or slow it down, or deflect its course. Aristotle, following the analogy of a horse drawing a cart, thought that if anything was in motion it

had to have something pushing or pulling it all the time—
he had no idea of its moving of its own impetus. This view
left the door half open for spirits at the very start—for
wherever anything was in motion you had to discover a
mover perpetually operating upon it. Dante imagines that
there are Intelligences that keep the spheres and the
heavenly bodies in motion. It was easy to turn the heavens,
because they were made of a special material without
weight or friction, and circular motion was natural to them
as we have seen. But in the Aristotelian physics that were
current until the seventeenth century it was impossible to
imagine anything that could move the heavy solid earth.
And it was this difficulty in the ancient physics that caused
the greatest obstruction to the scientists of the sixteenth
and seventeenth centuries.

II

WHY WAS SCIENCE
BACKWARD IN THE
MIDDLE AGES?

M. Postan

*Professor of Economic History
in the University of Cambridge*

I T is generally agreed that the Middle Ages preserved
for the use of later times the science of the ancients.
Therein lies both the scientific achievement and the scientific failure of the medieval civilisation. The achievement
was all the greater for being indirect. Men in the Dark Ages
did not find in the parts of the Western Empire which they
occupied a scientific tradition as rich as that which the
Arabs inherited in the eastern provinces. Scientific learning
came to them later, mostly in the twelfth and thirteenth
centuries, from the Arabs and the Jews. To have borrowed
and absorbed a scientific culture from peoples which were
at that time so distant and so alien was indeed a great
achievement. It was all that great, but no greater. What
the Middle Ages took over they did not very much enrich.
Indeed so small was their own contribution that historians
of science are apt to regard the Middle Ages as something
of a pause.

Needless to say, the pause was not undisturbed or un-
broken. In the course of centuries medieval men improved
somewhat their practical arts and added a little to their
understanding of nature: and in some periods, such as the
turn of the twelfth and thirteenth centuries, their own ad-

vances were sufficiently great to make it possible for us to speak of the scientific renaissance, or revival, in the Middle Ages. As a result of the revival, scientific knowledge became much richer than it had once been. As late as the early eleventh century medieval mathematics were still confined to simple computations, to an elementary theory of simple numbers, to some rudimentary propositions of pre-Pythagorean geometry, the use of the counting frame (the abacus), and perhaps to decimal fractions. But by the end of the thirteenth century mathematicians were tackling advanced problems of the geometry of Pythagoras, approaching the solution of cubic equations by the intersection of cones, discussing spherical trigonometry, and indeed approaching the very verge of differential calculus. In the same period the astrologists had not only absorbed the Ptolemaic astronomy of the ancients, but had also got to know the map of the skies and the courses of stars and planets, and had thereby prepared the great Copernican revolution in astronomy. Similarly the medieval alchemists had stumbled across some new facts about the properties of metals and gases, while the compilers of medieval lapidaries or lists of magic stones, of medieval herbals and of the medieval bestiaries, paved the way for the great scientific classifications of the sixteenth and seventeenth centuries. Some curious and learned men went even further than that. We have all heard about Frederick II's dissection of animals, but he was apparently not alone in this kind of investigation, for by the end of the Middle Ages dissectors and surgeons had accumulated a certain amount of new anatomical knowledge as well as a few rudimentary facts of human physiology. Now and again we find men engaging in practical tests which look like primitive experiments.

On the more practical plane we find here and there instances of great technical progress. Thus at the beginning of the medieval epoch, in the Dark Ages, the tillers of the soil were sufficiently enterprising to invent, or at least to adopt, what was at that time a brand-new system of agricultural technique—the rotation of crops by a two- or three-field system, the use of the heavy wheeled plough, and above all the modern system of harnessing animals from the shoulder, none of which had been known to the Romans or, if known, used extensively by them. During the same period the large water-mill, sometimes equipped with the overshot wheel and geared transmission, replaced in many parts of Europe the small horizontal water-mill of the so-called Irish or Norse type. It is also probable that, during the period of active land reclamation in Flanders during the tenth and eleventh, and in eastern Germany in the twelfth and thirteenth centuries, peasants adopted a more efficient lay-out of villages, an improved method of drainage, and possibly even more intensive forms of agriculture. We also find great technical ingenuity in mining and in the construction and improvements of implements of war, especially of machines for siege. Above all there was continuous technical progress in the greatest of medieval practical arts, in that of building. In the interval between the tenth and thirteenth centuries the technique of building developed much faster and went much further than during those four or five centuries of renaissance architecture which were to come between medieval buildings and the ferro-concrete structures of our own day.

Thus some advance on planes both purely intellectual and technical there was; yet taken together and placed against the vast panorama of medieval life, or indeed against the achievements of Greek and Hellenistic science in the fourth century B.C., or with the scientific activity of the seventeenth century, all these achievements are bound to appear very poor. Why then this poverty?

To this question many answers can be and have been given. But what most of them boil down to is the absence in medieval life of what I should be inclined to call scientific incentives. Students of science sometimes differ about the true inspiration of scientific progress. Some seek and find it in man's intellectual curiosity, in his desire to understand the workings of nature. Others believe that scientific knowledge grew and still grows out of man's attempts to improve his tools and his methods of production; that, in short, scientific truth is a by-product of technical progress. I do not want here to take sides in this particular controversy; what I want to suggest is that the Middle Ages were doubly unfortunate in that both the inspirations, the intellectual as well as the practical, failed more or less.

The easiest to account for is the intellectual. The Middle Ages were the age of faith, and to that extent they were unfavourable to scientific speculation. It is not that scientists as such were proscribed. For on the whole the persecution of men for their scientific ideas was very rare: rare because men with dangerous ideas, or indeed with any scientific ideas at all, were themselves very rare; and it is indeed surprising that there were any at all. This does not mean that there were no intellectual giants. All it means is that in an age which was one of faith, men of intellect and spirit found the calls of faith itself—its elucidation, its controversies, and its conquests—a task sufficient to absorb them. To put it simply, they had no time for occupations like science.

In fact they had neither the time nor the inclination. For even if there had been enough men to engage in activities as mundane as science, there would still be very little reason for them to do so. In times when medieval religious dogma stood whole and unshaken the intellectual objects and the methods of science were, to say the least, superfluous. The purpose of scientific enquiry is to build up piecemeal a unified theory of the universe, of its origin and of its working. But in the Middle Ages was that process really necessary? Did not medieval man already possess in God, in the story of Creation and in the doctrine of Omnipotent Will, a complete explanation of how the world came about and of how, by what means and to what purpose, it was being conducted? Why build up in laborious and painstaking mosaic a design which was already there from the outset, clear and visible to all?

So much for intellectual incentive. The practical incentive was almost equally feeble. Greater understanding of nature could not come from technical improvements, chiefly because technical improvements were so few. Medieval occupations continued for centuries without appreciable change of method. After the great period of initial development, i.e. after the late eleventh century, the routine of medieval farming in the greater part of Europe became as fixed as the landscape itself. In the history of the smithies, the weav-

ing shops, or the potteries, there were occasional periods
of innovation, but taking the Middle Ages as a whole technical improvement was very rare and very slow.

For this medieval economic policy was largely to blame.
In the course of centuries, economic activities got surrounded with a vast structure of bye-laws and regulations.
In the villages regulations were necessary in order to guar-
antee to the landlords that their tenants would be able to
pay or to work off their dues, but also in order to secure the
rights and obligations of individual members of a village
community. In most towns of the later Middle Ages there
were regulations to secure fair prices, to maintain wages, to
lay down standards of quality, and above all, to protect
individual masters from competition. But, however necessary or commendable these objects may have been, they
made technical improvement very difficult. For bye-laws
were as a rule based on the technical methods in existence
when they were framed; and once framed they were to
stand in the way of all subsequent change.

What is more, so deeply ingrained was the spirit of pro-
tection that in every local trade the technical methods were
treated as a secret. The medieval craft gild described itself
as a 'mystery' and often was one. To take an example, the
prosperity of the Bologna silk industry, famous all over
Europe, was in its early stages due to many new processes
and labour-saving devices. But it is characteristic of medieval technology that the machine for throwing silk which
was invented in 1272 by Borghesano of Bologna (and was
certainly employed in the Bolognese silk industry in the
later Middle Ages) was not to be known outside Bologna
until 1538, and was not effectively imitated until a travelling Englishman obtained its designs by ruse in the seventeenth century. Much of the specialised local skill of certain
areas of medieval Europe was rooted in knowledge carefully
guarded from outsiders. It is for that reason that industries
with advanced techniques, e.g. mining or cloth finishing,
seldom spread to new areas except by mass migration and
resettlement of the men who practised them.

It is thus no wonder that knowledge painfully acquired
in industrial practice so seldom percolated into the realm

of science, while the scientific knowledge of the scholars so seldom influenced the industrial technique. Thus the main qualities of iron had been discovered and its resilience known at the very dawn of the Middle Ages and before, but we have no record of the leaf spring until the seventeenth century or of the spiral spring until the fifteenth. For several hundred years after the appearance in Europe of Arab numerals, and for at least a hundred and fifty years after the earlier western treatises explaining their use in computation, commercial and state accountancy still employed the awkward Roman numerals. On the other hand, for centuries after the pump, especially in its simpler syringe form, was employed in industry, the development of theoretical mechanics floundered in error through the failure to employ the concept of vacuum. None of the experience accumulated and utilised in the construction of appliances, mostly military, employing the pressure of water and air, or the expansion of heated air and steam, was capable of affecting the official theory of hydrostatics or of suggesting a theory of the expansion of gases or of atmospheric pressure. And although levers, both curved and straight, had been employed in construction since time immemorial, mechanics did not arrive at the concept of 'moment of force' until about the end of the thirteenth century. The practical knowledge of the medieval farmers and stockbreeders remained virtually without effect on biological theory, the experience of the dyers and the fullers remained without effect on the chemical theories. Medieval technology and medieval science each kept to their carefully circumscribed spheres.

Indeed, nothing exemplifies this general condition of technical stagnation better than the exceptions I have already mentioned. The great agricultural innovations of the early Middle Ages took place at the time when medieval population was still, so to speak, on the move, and when the medieval economic organisation and its laws had not yet taken shape. Agricultural innovations of a later age, such as the Flemish and German of the twelfth and thirteenth centuries, were part and parcel of the colonisation movement, i.e. were only possible because society was again on the move. The great technical discoveries in industrial occupations took place only when and where the industry happened to be beyond the reach of local authority. The technology of war was in the service of princes, and princes were not bound by the social aims or economic objectives of medieval gilds. The great technical changes in the English cloth industry in the fourteenth century were made possible only by the flight of the industry from the towns to the villages over which the authority of municipalities did not extend. Above all, medieval building was in the hands of masons who were 'free', free in the sense that they were migratory labourers seldom subject to supervision and technical control by town governments.

In spheres more purely intellectual, the quickening of scientific activity in the late twelfth and thirteenth centuries, the so-called medieval renaissance, was also in some respects exceptional. It will be a mistake to put it down solely to the influx of translations. The translations, far from explaining the scientific activity, themselves require an explanation. For at least three hundred years the Arabs had been there with their versions of ancient philosophy, while the contacts with them were not necessarily closer in 1250 than they had been, say, in 850. Yet neither in the early centuries of the Middle Ages nor in its closing centuries was there a comparable flow of translations.

How are we then to account for the spate in the thirteenth century? Certainly not by the Italian trade in the Levant or by the Crusades. Few of the translations came from the Levant; hardly any were the work of Crusaders or of the Italian merchants or of anybody in their service. A cause more fundamental and more directly intellectual was obviously at work. For, unless I am mistaken, the intellectual climate in the middle centuries of the Middle Ages had changed. It is even possible that, for the time being, faith itself did not wholly absorb the interests of men. Mundane and secular preoccupations, both literary and philosophical, suddenly appeared amidst a culture still mainly religious. Within religion itself minority movements of every kind, including those of the early friars, disturbed more than ever before the uniformity of ideas. Disagreements appeared at the very centres of medieval learning, philosophical controversies seemed to shake the very foundations of dogma, and behind some of the milder manifestations of dissent lurked the possibilities of the profoundest scepticism and doubt. No wonder a Frenchman, Taine, described the whole period as an epoch tormented by doubt. And from the doubts of the thirteenth century, as from similar doubts in later ages, there was bound to issue a current of intellectual curiosity, a willingness to re-open questions which hitherto appeared closed, and to seek answers from every source capable of giving them. Hence the revived interest in the philosophical and scientific doctrines of antiquity; hence the eagerness to learn from the Greeks and Arabs; hence also the translations.

In this way the very achievement of the late twelfth and thirteenth centuries merely underlines the verdict about the Middle Ages as a whole. The men of the Middle Ages were unable to do more than they did because they were lacking in scientific incentive. What they achieved in advancing the practical arts of humanity or in preserving and transmitting ancient learning, they did in so far and as long as they were not typically medieval.

III

COPERNICUS AND
THE PLANETS

Herbert Dingle

*Professor of the History and Philosophy of Science
in the University of London*

T HE work with which I am going to deal is the outstanding example in history of the tremendous consequences that can follow a very slight change in our way of looking at things. The Copernican revolution, as it is sometimes called, is the supreme symbol of the passage from the medieval to the modern world, from an outlook which now seems like that of fairyland to the matter-of-fact outlook of the present day; yet it involved no great discovery, no new idea, and caused no abrupt change in the philosophy even of its originator. Its whole importance lies in what it made possible. We will try to see how this happened, but first let us take a brief glance at Copernicus himself.

Copernicus was one of those universal geniuses of whom former times afford several examples, but who in our complex modern life can scarcely any longer appear. Churchman, statesman, scholar, lawyer, artist, poet, physician, economist, mathematician, astronomer—he was all these things, but his ruling passion—if passion is the right word for so mild and gentle a thinker—was mathematical astronomy. He was born in 1473 at Toruń in Poland. After a prolonged education, first in the University of Cracow and then at Bologna and Rome, he returned in 1506, at the age of 33 years, to take up duties as Canon of Frauenburg

Cathedral, and there until his death in 1543 he pursued his various activities as occasion demanded, but with the perfection of his astronomical system always at the back of his mind.

What was that system? As you know, the people of his time thought of the Earth as fixed at the centre of a universe of spheres which revolved with perfect regularity round it. The heavenly bodies—Sun, Moon, stars and planets—were attached to the spheres and showed by their movements how the spheres moved, but in a very indirect way. A particular planet (Mars, for instance) showed only the resultant movement of many spheres, each with its own radius, axis and rate of revolution. It therefore appeared to move very irregularly, but since the spheres themselves were invisible it gave the only available clue to their number and character. The problem of astronomy was thus to discover what combination of uniformly moving spheres could produce the movements seen, and this problem, applied to all the bodies in the sky, had engaged the attention of astronomers for 1400 years.

Now this view of things was not the result of guesswork or stupid prejudice. In the time of the early Greeks there was no such universally accepted scheme, and even the first element of it—the fixed central position of the Earth—was a matter for enquiry and discussion. Certainly appearances suggested that the Earth was fixed and stationary, but some thinkers—notably Aristarchus of Samos in the third century B.C.—held that the Earth not only rotated about an axis but also moved in an orbit round the Sun, and that the appearances of movements in the sky were simply consequences of these movements of the Earth. However, in the second century A.D., Ptolemy of Alexandria made a judicial enquiry into the whole matter. He seriously considered the possibility of the Earth's movement, but rejected it on grounds which to him appeared final and which, with the knowledge he had, were certainly reasonable. Thereafter the principle of the geocentric universe was generally accepted, and the system grew more and more elaborate as more and more spheres were added to account for the irregularities which the movements of the heavenly bodies went on revealing.

It was the extreme complexity into which the system had grown by the end of the fifteenth century that offended the mathematical mind of Copernicus. By that time more than eighty spheres were found necessary 'to save appearances', as the phrase went—i.e. to account for the observed movements—and, even so, the movements were not completely explained. It seemed to Copernicus unlikely that God, who could do all things perfectly, would make such an ugly universe, and he accordingly turned back to the long dis-credited idea that the Earth moved, to see if, by thus re-lieving the spheres of some movements, he could account for the rest by a simpler system. He soon saw that this was possible, and for some thirty years, in season and out, he worked unceasingly to devise a new universe, pencilling his ideas on scraps of paper, the margins of books, and even on walls, until he had completed a scheme which not only explained all that Ptolemy's scheme had done, but did so more exactly and with only thirty-four spheres. He told the whole story in a great work—*De Revolutionibus Orbium Caelestium* ('On the Revolutions of the Heavenly Spheres' —not heavenly *bodies*, but heavenly *spheres*)—of which we are told the earliest copy was brought to him as he lay on his death-bed.

It is often said that Copernicus was afraid to publish his work during his life-time from fear of persecution, but there is no evidence for this. He did in fact circulate a short account of it in manuscript form in his *Commentariolus* many years before his death, and in 1540 he allowed his pupil Rheticus to print a preliminary statement of the sys-tem. Moreover, his work was well known to the Pope and others high in the Councils of the Roman Church, and greatly admired. What actually deterred Copernicus was fear of ridicule. At that time it seemed so obvious that the Earth was at rest that anyone who asserted the contrary would certainly become the object of foolish jokes, and this he was too sensitive and retiring to risk. He accordingly told his ideas only to those who could appreciate the reasons for them.

Why was it, then, that a century after his death his work became the centre of one of the most violent intellectual controversies that the world has known? The reason was that, though apparently simple and harmless, it in fact gave the death-blow to the whole medieval system of thought, for it touched that system at its most vital spot. It is hard for us to realise today, when so many quite dissimilar departments of knowledge surround us on all sides, that medi-

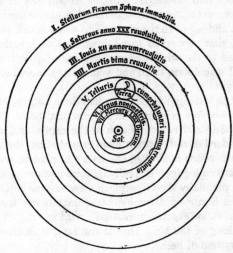

I. Stellarum Fixarum Sphæra immobilis.
II. Saturnus anno XXX reuoluitur.
III. Iouis XII annorumreuolutio
IIII. Martis bima reuolutio.
V. Telluris cũ orbe lunari annua reuolutio
VI. Venus nonimestris.
VII. Mercury LXXX dierum.
Sol.

THE UNIVERSE ACCORDING TO COPERNICUS (1543)

eval thought was essentially a unity. The subjects we know as astronomy, physics, chemistry, theology, psychology, physiology, and so on, were then all fused together in a single system. Above the outermost sphere of astronomy was the heaven of theology, pictured in the same diagram. The stars were not remote globes of gas; they affected men's temperaments and to some extent controlled their destinies. The planets had affinities with the earthly metals. Human bodies represented the universe on a smaller scale. For instance, as you learned in the opening chapter of this book, everything that we call 'matter' was supposed by medieval thinkers to be made up of four elements—earth, water, air, fire—mixed in various degrees; in liquids, for example, water predominated, and in solids, earth. Similarly, human temperaments were made up of four so-called 'humours' mixed in various degrees, and according as one or another predominated so you were phlegmatic, choleric, sanguine or melancholy. Thus the humours were to what we should call the mental world what the elements were to the material world, and the parallel was so close that you may remember that Shakespeare makes Antony say of Brutus: 'The elements . . . so mixed in him that nature might stand up . . . and say to all the world "This was a man".' Nothing, in fact, that concerned men's lives here or hereafter was unrelated to the whole scheme of things. Upset the astronomical machinery, then, and you destroy the whole body of thought.

Now at first sight Copernicus had done nothing to upset the astronomical machinery in any essential point. True, he put the Sun and not the Earth at the centre and made it the standard of rest, but the main organisation, the spheres of heaven which controlled the stars and planets, were still there performing their eternally uniform motions, and by its greater simplicity the Copernican view seemed to establish still more firmly a philosophy that ultimately saw the whole universe as an expression of God's wisdom. But in fact it did nothing of the kind. On the contrary, it destroyed the whole system of belief.

To see how this was so, let us ask ourselves why the spheres were ever supposed to exist. They were not seen or directly observed in any way; why, then, were they believed to be there? If you imagine the Earth to be at rest and watch the sky for a few hours, you will have no difficulty in answering this question. You will see a host of stars, all moving in circles round a single axis at precisely the same rate of about one revolution a day. You cannot then believe that each one moves independently of the others, and that their motions just happen to have this relation to one another. No one but a lunatic would doubt that he was looking at the revolution of a single sphere with all the stars attached to it. And if the stars had a sphere, then the Sun, Moon and planets, whose movements were almost the same, would also be moved by the same kind of mechanism. The existence of the spheres having thus been established and accepted implicitly for century after century, men no longer thought of the reasons which demanded them, but took them for granted as facts of experience; and Copernicus himself, despite his long years of meditation on the fundamental problems of astronomy, never dreamed of doubting their existence.

But actually, you see, he had destroyed the whole basis of it. In his system the movements of the stars which were so closely related to one another were taken away from them and given to the Earth. But, that being so, why assume that the stars were attached to a sphere? The appearance would be the same if there were no sphere and even if the stars were at various distances, provided that those distances were very great. There was no reason, in fact, why space should not extend outwards without limit, with stars scattered at random all the way. And if the stars had no sphere, why should the planets have them? These thoughts were bound to arise sooner or later, and arise they did. In the century after the death of Copernicus, Bruno taught the doctrine of an infinite universe, without centre, in which the innumerable stars were Suns; Kepler discarded the circular motions which the spheres demanded and described the orbits of the planets as ellipses; Galileo with his telescope saw the Milky Way as a realisation of Bruno's vision and discovered satellites of Jupiter which would have had to move through Jupiter's sphere if it had had one. In short, the spheres became thoroughly discredited, and with them went the whole edifice of medieval thought.

We can hardly imagine today the effect of such a change on the minds of thoughtful men in the sixteenth century. It is scarcely possible that anything like it can ever occur again because, as I have said, our knowledge is now so divided into separate departments that whatever fundamental change may occur in one will leave most of the rest almost untouched. But the Copernican revolution upset everything —the whole medieval system of thought. With the spheres went a localised heaven for the souls of the blessed, the distinction between celestial and sublunar matter and motion became meaningless, the whole place of man in the cosmic scheme became uncertain.

Take astrology—the belief that the details of men's temperaments and careers were appreciably affected by the movements of the heavenly bodies. This had fallen, by the middle of the seventeenth century, from the recognised science it had been to the superstition it is today, although, of course, it was still widely practised by the unenlightened. Can you see why? Here are the lines on which the argument for astrology would run. It was irreverent to suppose that God had created useless bodies, and therefore, with man as the centre of creation, it followed that the planets had a human significance—an influence on man—which we might reasonably try to discover. But once the Earth is seen to be but a minor planet of a minor star in an infinite host of stars, and man anything but the centre of creation, the whole argument falls to the ground. Why should the planets in such a system influence the affairs of men? They might have other much more important work to do, of which we knew nothing. It is small wonder, then, that, when the overwhelming implications of the Copernican view became realised, it was resisted by all the means thought appropriate at the time. It inevitably appeared at first as purely destructive, and destructive of everything worth preserving. We can see it today in another light. To us it is not only the end of one intellectual age but the necessary preparation for another—the scientific age in which we are now thoroughly immersed. Copernicus himself was in no sense the originator of modern science. He was thoroughly medieval in outlook, and had he been able to foresee what his work was to do we may well believe that he would have shrunk in the utmost horror from the responsibility which he would have felt. But what he did was to make it possible for the new scientific philosophy to emerge.

In brief, what happened was this. Between Ptolemy and Copernicus no question arose in men's minds concerning the meaning of motion. It was obvious: if a body was changing its position with respect to the Earth it was moving; otherwise it was at rest. But after Copernicus, whatever view you took, you had to consider the possibility that motion meant something else—namely, change of position with respect to the Sun. You made your choice and argued against the other view, but at least you thereby acknowledged that it stood in need of defeat by argument and was not a manifest absurdity. It was just this state of affairs that made it possible for Galileo, at the beginning of the seventeenth century, to propound his doctrine of 'local motion', which became the foundation of science. According to this doctrine, if you had any number of bodies, all moving at different constant speeds, you could take any one you liked to be at rest. It was idle to ask which body was *really* stationary, because it was entirely a matter of convenience.

A simple example may give us some idea of the simplification thus introduced into the study of motion. When you are in a train moving smoothly at 60 miles an hour, everything happens just as though you were sitting in your room at home. You can read and write in comfort and throw a ball into the air and catch it as it comes down. Hence, said Galileo in effect, you may take the train to be at rest, and if you walk along the corridor at an ordinary pace you may say quite truly that you are walking at the rate of 6 ft. a second—that is, ordinary walking pace, about 4 miles an hour. Before Copernicus, however, such a statement would not have been held to be true; in one second you would really have walked 94 ft., not six. That is to say, your speed would have been reckoned as your walking speed (6 ft. per second) plus the train's speed (88 ft. per second). The calculation in this case is not difficult, but when you take into account many bodies moving in different directions at different speeds, not all uniform, the complications that would result if you had to reduce them all to the standard of the Earth would have made it impossible to discover any laws of motion at all.

Newton took advantage of the liberty which this idea provided, as you will read in a later chapter. When he was considering the motion of the planets he took the Sun to be at rest, as Copernicus held, but when he was considering the fall of an apple to the ground he took the Earth to be at rest, as the anti-Copernicans held. He was then able to show that the same general law of gravitation held for the planets as for the apple, and to build on Galileo's principle the general laws of motion on which almost all subsequent science rests. The story has no end as yet because we cannot even guess what further developments of science will bring. But whatever it may be, we know, from the very nature of science itself, that it will necessarily grow out of what has gone before. So when you hear in the future of the new knowledge that is coming to light, and perhaps take part in discovering it, remember that it has all become possible because of the ideas of a man who thought he was simplifying the established scheme of the world, and who changed the course of the world's thought for ever.

IV

BACON AND THE
EXPERIMENTAL METHOD

C. D. Broad, LITT.D., F.B.A.

*Knightbridge Professor of Moral Philosophy
in the University of Cambridge*

I WILL begin by giving you a very brief sketch of Bacon's life, so that you may have some idea of the kind of man that he was and the society in which he moved. He was born at York House, Strand, London, in January 1561, i.e. about two years after Queen Elizabeth came to the throne. His father was Nicholas Bacon, who held the office of Lord Keeper; and his mother was Anne Cook, whose father had been tutor to Edward VI. So we may say that Bacon's family belonged to the higher ranks of the civil service. Bacon was a very bright precocious boy, and Queen Elizabeth used to enjoy talking to him. He was sent to Cambridge as an undergraduate of Trinity College at the extremely early age of thirteen, and he left two years later. He then took up the study and practice of law, which became his profession. The Queen employed him much in legal and political business, but she seems not to have really liked him or trusted him, and he held no important office under her reign. After the accession of James I in 1603 Bacon's advancement was rapid, for the King greatly admired him. He became Lord Keeper, Lord Chancellor, and in 1620 Viscount St. Albans. He was now a very wealthy man, but a tragedy was approaching. He had always been careless with money and extravagant in his mode of life, and he had followed the common practice of his day in taking presents from suitors, though he always asserted that he had not allowed this to influence his legal judgments. However that may be, he was tried on a charge of corruption, pleaded guilty, was condemned, and had to pay a fine of £40,000 (an immense sum in those days), lost his office, and was banished from the court. This happened in 1621. Bacon lived on for another five years, a broken man. He died in April 1626. His last illness is said to have been caused by his getting out of his carriage in freezingly cold weather in order to try the experiment of stuffing the carcase of a fowl with snow to test the preservative effects of a low temperature.

Though Bacon was an able, and up to a point successful, lawyer and politician, his heart was not in that work. His one fundamental interest was to discover and propagate a general method by which men might gain scientific knowledge of the ultimate laws and structure of matter, and might thus acquire ever-increasing practical control over nature. He saw that, in order to collect the data from which the laws of nature were to be extracted by his methods, a huge organisation of research would be needed. Vast numbers of men and women, at various levels, would have to be employed, and expensive buildings and apparatus would be required. All this would be very costly. The only hope of getting adequate supplies of money and sufficient authority and prestige to start and continue such a scheme was for Bacon himself to become a rich and prominent man and for him to persuade the King and powerful noblemen and churchmen to back it. In order to do this he must be ready to turn a blind eye to their vices and follies, to humour their whims, and to play upon their weaknesses by flattery. Bacon was nothing if not thorough, and he analysed and practised with his usual acuteness and assiduity the arts of worldly success. I believe that, like many other clever idealistic men, he started by seeking wealth and power wholly, or at any rate mainly, as a means to a high impersonal end, but gradually slipped into pursuing them for their own sake. I suspect also that, as often happens with such men, *he* was not quite so clever, and those whom he used and despised were not quite so stupid as he imagined, and that he was seen through and distrusted much more than he realised.

If we are to appreciate Bacon's originality, farsightedness and breadth of vision and to be fair to his limitations and mistakes, we must see him against the background of the science of his own day and not against that of ours. The fundamental science of dynamics, for instance, did not exist. It was founded during Bacon's life-time by Galileo (1564–1642), who also invented the telescope and noted with it the spots on the sun and the irregularities on the moon's surface. In astronomy it was still generally held that the earth is the fixed centre of the universe, and that the sun and the planets revolved about it, the latter in complicated epicyclic orbits. The discovery of the three fundamental laws of planetary motion was made in Bacon's life-time by Kepler (1571–1630). It was not until long after Bacon's death that Newton provided the first example of a scientific theory on the grand scale and in the modern sense, by explaining those laws and correlating them with the phenomena of falling bodies through his hypothesis of universal gravitation. Bacon's older contemporary Gilbert (1540–1603) had discovered some elementary facts about natural magnets, but the existence of electricity was unknown and its connexion with magnetism was unsuspected. Chemistry, as a science and not a mere set of recipes, did not come into existence for another hundred and fifty years. Learned men commonly accepted without question the Aristotelian theory that earthly bodies are composed of the four elements, earth, air, fire and water, and that heavenly bodies are fundamentally different, being composed of a superior fifth element, called the *quintessence*.

Corresponding to this lack of scientific knowledge was a lack of power over nature. The only available devices for obtaining mechanical energy were clockwork, waterwheels, and windmills. All land transport was on foot or by horse, and all water transport by rowing or sailing. Men were constantly at the mercy of local and seasonal food shortages and gluts, and were periodically decimated by epidemics, whose causes they did not understand and which they had no rational means of combating. Bacon was impressed by

this impotence and its evil consequences, and he could not
be expected to foresee, what we have learned since, that
men can bring even greater evils upon themselves by abus-
ing the power which science gives them than they suffered
when they were powerless in face of natural forces.

Now Bacon was completely convinced that the ignorance
of nature and the consequent lack of power over nature,
which had prevailed from the earliest times up to his day,
were by no means inevitable. They sprang, not from any
fundamental imperfection in the human mind, nor from
lawlessness or inextricable complexity in nature, but simply and solely from the use of a wrong method. He felt sure
that he knew the right method, and that, if only this could
be substituted and applied on a large enough scale, there
was no limit to the possible growth of human knowledge
and human power over nature. Looking back after the
event, we can see that he was right, and we may be tempted
to think that it was obvious. But it was not in the least
obvious at the time; it was, on the contrary, a most remarkable feat of insight and an act of rational faith in the
face of present appearances and past experience.

What was wrong with the methods in use up to Bacon's
time? The fundamental defects, as Bacon clearly saw, were
the following. In the first place there was an almost complete divorce between theory, observation and experiment,
and practical application. Plenty of experiments of a kind
had been done, and a certain number of disconnected em-
pirical rules or recipes had been discovered. But the experiments were made in the main by men like alchemists
and quack-salvers. These were often, though by no means
always, charlatans or half-crazy enthusiasts. But, even
when they were honest and sensible men, they did their
experiments with some immediate practical end in view,
such as turning lead into gold or discovering a universal
medicine for all diseases. They were not guided by any
general theory; they did not seek to discover the all-
pervading laws and the minute structure of matter; and
they worked in isolation from each other, keeping their results secret rather than pooling them. Bacon valued science
both as an end in itself and for the immense power over

nature which he believed that it could give. He thought
that the failure of contemporary physics to have any useful
practical applications was a sign that it was on the wrong
track. But he was firmly convinced that it is fatal for scientists to work shortsightedly at the solution of this or that
particular problem. Let them concentrate, he thought, on
discovering by suitably designed experiments and appropriate reasoning the fundamental laws and structure of nature.
Then, and only then, could they make innumerable practical applications with complete certainty of success. Anyone
who reflects on how our modern applications of electro-
magnetism, of chemistry, and of medicine depend respectively on the theoretical work of Faraday and Maxwell, of
Dalton and Avogadro, and of Pasteur, will see how right
Bacon was in this.

The second defect which Bacon found in the science of
his time was on the theoretical side. During the twelfth
century, when Europe had reawakened from barbarism and
men had again begun to take a scientific interest in external
nature, it happened that the works on physics of the Greek
philosopher Aristotle were re-discovered. It happened also
that the greatest and most influential thinker of the Middle
Ages, St. Thomas Aquinas (1226–1274), became an enthusiastic disciple and advocate of Aristotle. Now St.
Thomas was a daring innovator who had to face strong
opposition. But Aristotle's physics and logic were so much
better than anything else available at the time, and St.
Thomas was so much abler than his opponents, that the
Aristotelian methods and concepts scored a complete triumph. Thenceforth they were accepted uncritically and
handed down from one generation to another. Scientists de-
cided all questions, not by investigating the observable facts,
but by appealing to the infallible authority of Aristotle, just
as present-day Communists appeal to that of Marx, and
Engels and Lenin. Now this would have been disastrous,
even if Aristotle's physics had been sound. But although he
was a very great man, his strength lay in natural history
and in certain branches of deductive logic. He was no mathematician, and his theories of physics and astronomy were
much inferior to those of certain other Greek philosophers.

Bacon rightly accused the learned men of his time of accepting on authority sweeping general principles, which Aristotle himself had reached by hasty and uncritical generalisation from a few rather superficial observations. Using these as premisses, they proceeded to deduce conclusions about nature and to hold elaborate wrangles with each other by means of Aristotle's favourite form of reasoning, which is called the 'syllogism'. The following argument is an example of a valid syllogism: All metals are good conductors of heat, and all good conductors of electricity are metals; therefore all good conductors of electricity are good conductors of heat. Some arguments in syllogistic form are valid and others are not. Aristotle formulated the rules for distinguishing between valid and invalid syllogistic arguments. That was a very considerable achievement, but, to put it familiarly, it rather 'went to his head', and made him overestimate the importance of the syllogism. What he failed to do was to suggest any method for establishing generalisations, like 'All metals are good conductors of heat', which are needed as premisses before any syllogistic argument can get started.

Bacon saw that syllogistic reasoning, however well it may be adapted for tripping up an opponent in the law courts or in Parliament, is utterly useless for discovering the laws of nature and for applying them to the solution of practical problems. What was wanted was a method by which we could slowly and cautiously rise from observed facts to wider and deeper generalisations, testing every such generalisation at each stage by deliberately looking out for possible exceptions to it, and rejecting or modifying it if we actually found such exceptions.

That process is called 'induction'. Of course, as Bacon quite well knew, men have always been practising it to a certain extent in an unconscious and unsystematic way. What Bacon did was to abstract and exhibit the general principles of such reasoning, so that in future men might perform it consciously with a full knowledge of what they were doing. Perhaps his greatest service here was to show the importance of testing every generalisation by devising and performing experiments which would refute it if the result turned out in a certain way, and would confirm it if the result turned out in a certain other way.

Bacon realised that every man inherits or acquires certain mental kinks, of which he is generally quite unaware. These tend to lead us astray in our thinking, and we need to be put on our guard against them. Bacon calls these kinks by the quaint name of 'Idols'. Besides the tendency to accept on authority the dogmas of some prominent person or sect, which Bacon calls 'Idols of the Theatre', he enumerates three others. 'Idols of the Tribe' are certain unfortunate mental tendencies common to the whole human race: for instance, the tendency to notice facts which support one's beliefs and fall in with one's wishes, and to ignore or pervert those which do not. Then there are 'Idols of the Market Place'. These arise from the fact that many words and phrases embody the false beliefs and inaccurate observations of our remote ancestors, and are thus, so to speak, crystallised errors which we swallow unconsciously. Lastly, there are 'Idols of the Cave'. These are sources of error or bias which are peculiar to each individual, depending on his particular temperament and the special circumstances of his upbringing.

It is time for me to bring this chapter about Bacon to an end, though there is much more that I would like to tell you about him and his work. In conclusion I would say that he was not a practising scientist, and it would be quite unfair to judge him from that point of view. His service to science was to criticise the existing bad methods, to try to formulate the methods which should be substituted for them, and to paint a glowing picture of the power which men might acquire by such means over nature. Perhaps his main defect here was his failure to see the enormously important part which mathematics was to play in the development of science. But in other respects he showed great insight and most remarkable foresight, and he clothed his thoughts in a garment of wit and wisdom which makes his writings one of the glories of English literature.

V

HARVEY AND THE
CIRCULATION OF
THE BLOOD

Sir Henry Dale, O.M., G.B.E., F.R.S.

*Formerly Director of the
National Institute for Medical Research*

I SUPPOSE that nearly everybody has heard that William Harvey discovered the circulation of the blood. To most people it will be clear that such a discovery would have been a major event in the development of the knowledge required for the practice of medicine. I think that many are aware, indeed, that in William Harvey's publication, in 1628, of the conclusions to which his researches had led him, in a wonderful little book with the title *An Anatomical Treatise on the Movement of the Heart and the Blood*, we can find the very beginning of medical science in the modern sense. Harvey's work, however, had a much wider importance for the whole range of the natural sciences; it was one of the earliest and most convincing applications of what, in his own time, was still the new and even revolutionary method of studying nature by direct observation and experiment. For, as you will have read in earlier chapters, during more than a thousand years there had been practically no attempt made by the inhabitants of Europe to find out the facts of nature for themselves. Philosophers of Ancient Greece had made observations and constructed theories which, being transmitted with the authority of the Church, had acquired the force of dogmas. In physiology, which was Harvey's most direct concern, the writings of Aristotle to some extent, but more particularly those of the Greek physician Galen, had thus, for many centuries, been

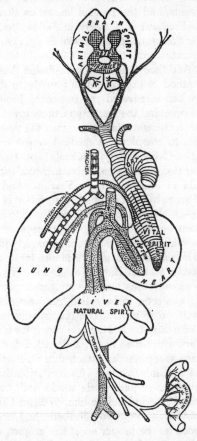

THE BLOOD SYSTEM ACCORDING TO GALEN

imposed as final and authoritative, so that it had been impious and even dangerous to challenge them.

By Harvey's time, the fetters by which men's thoughts about nature had thus so long been shackled had begun to loosen and to fall. Within one month in the year 1543 there had been two events of tremendous significance in the history of science. Copernicus had laid the foundation of modern astronomy with his scheme of the motions of the earth and the planets, and the Belgian known as Vesalius, who was then a Professor of Surgery in Padua, published his book on *The Structure of the Human Body*, giving the first full and accurate description of its anatomy, based on actual dissections. And then Galileo, another Padua Professor, had used the method of experiment to investigate the laws of motion and had discovered the moons of Jupiter with a simple telescope; and the memory of these great men must still have been cherished in Padua when the young Harvey arrived there to complete his medical education, after he had studied at Caius College in Cambridge. Harvey's own teacher of anatomy at Padua, Fabricius, was the successor in the Chair, at one remove, to Vesalius. And Fabricius himself had given the first complete description of the valves in the veins—an observation which was later to be used by Harvey, when he demonstrated the passage of the blood through the veins in one direction only, namely towards the heart, as an important item of his evidence for its circulation round the body. So that Harvey, while he was studying in Padua, was already breathing the invigorating air of what, in England, was soon to be called 'the new philosophy'— the doctrine, then so new, that a man should improve his knowledge of nature by looking and trying for himself.

When Harvey returned home, and settled down to practise in London as a physician attached to St. Bartholomew's Hospital, he certainly carried with him an enthusiasm for this new approach to nature. He would find, indeed, that it had reached England before him. William Gilbert, who had been physician to Queen Elizabeth, had already published his book on the properties of the magnet, describing a remarkable series of observations and experiments which he had made, and laying the foundation for all later acquisition of knowledge concerning magnetism. Francis Bacon, too, must have been preparing to give to the world the great philosophical treatises in which he so convincingly advocated the direct approach to nature, the attainment of natural knowledge by induction from accumulated observations and by bringing theory to the test of experiment. It is curious, indeed, to note that Bacon, who became one of Harvey's patients, never showed, even in his later writings, any awareness that the very methods which he was so forcefully recommending had already been used to such great purpose by Harvey, his own physician. Harvey, on his part, is reported as saying, disrespectfully, that Bacon wrote philosophy—by which, of course, he meant experimental science—'like a lord Chancellor'. But Harvey himself made, without explicit reference to Bacon, professions of faith and determination concerning the methods by which he would advance scientific knowledge, which are at least in good harmony with Bacon's theories. 'Not from books, but from dissections'—thus Harvey proclaims his method, in the introduction to his book on the heart and the circulation. And in the later and much larger book, in which he published observations and the results of experiments on the *Reproduction of Animals,* accumulated over many years, he makes an even more striking profession of his faith in the new method and of his contempt for the old one. 'It were disgraceful, therefore,' writes Harvey, 'with this most spacious and admirable realm of nature before us, did we take the reports of others upon trust and go on coining crude problems out of these, and on them hanging knotty and captious and petty disputations. Nature is herself to be addressed; the paths she shows us are to be boldly trodden; for thus, and while we consult our own senses, from lower advancing to higher levels, shall we penetrate at length into the heart of her mystery.'

It was in that spirit, then, that Harvey set to work on his enquiry concerning the movement of the heart and the blood when he returned to England. But, to understand what he achieved, we ought first to try to form some idea of the state of knowledge when he began. The diagram on page 35 will help you to understand the ideas of Galen which, fantastic as they seem to us, were still largely dominant. The products of the food, absorbed from the stomach and intestines, were supposed to be carried by the portal vein to the liver, there to be elaborated into blood and shed into the great vein, the *vena cava,* and thus carried to the right side of the heart, by the expansion of which the blood was supposed to be sucked into its cavity. With the contraction of the heart it was supposed to pass out again, most of it back along the *vena cava* and its branches to the body at large, but some by the 'artery-like vein', which we now call the pulmonary artery, to the lungs. Thus there was pictured a kind of ebb and flow of blood, to and from the right side of the heart, as it expanded and contracted. But how, then, could the blood get to the other, the left side of the heart, and so into the great artery of the body, the aorta and its branches? That was, perhaps, the most remarkable feature of Galen's scheme, and the one which throws most light on the type of evidence on which a theory could then be based, and accepted as final, for many centuries. Galen just assumed that the thick, fleshy septum between the right and left ventricles of the heart, though it seemed so solid, must be penetrated by pores, through which the blood could pass from right to left; and then from the left side it would flow and ebb with the heart's pulsation, by the aorta to and from the body at large, and by the vein-like arteries, which we now call the pulmonary veins, to and from the lungs. There was a complication in the scheme, connected with the doctrine of the natural, animal and vital spirits, vague qualities which were supposed to be conferred upon the blood by the liver, the brain and the heart itself; and there was another involved by the assumption that air as well as blood was sucked into the heart through the pulmonary veins. The essential features, however, were the passage of the blood to the body and the lungs and back again, to and from both sides of the heart, and by the veins as well as by the arteries; and then, to get the blood from the right to the left side of the heart, its passage through the septum by pores which nobody had ever seen. It is remarkable that even Vesalius, who looked for the pores and even recorded his failure to find them, had not the courage openly to discredit their existence; and that Fabricius, though he described the valves in the veins and showed them to his pupil Harvey, did not venture to suggest that they were competent valves, preventing the blood from flowing away from the heart by the veins, but only supposed that they retarded it, to keep it from flowing too fast in that direction. He, too, was still a pious believer in Galen.

We must note further, however, that, even before Harvey, other observers, and most clearly the Italian known as Cesalpino, appear to have been on the very verge of discovering the complete scheme of the double circulation, which Harvey's experiments were to reveal. And there, in all probability, we have the real clue to the failure even of Cesalpino, who had come so near to the truth, to arrive at a full understanding of it. For he was no experimenter; he was just a man of deep learning in philosophy and the sciences of his day, with a particular passion for theology and a love of argument. Neither his writings, therefore, nor those of his predecessors, had any important effect on the beliefs of their contemporaries, and it has required an antiquarian effort, in more recent times, to rediscover them and to show how significant they might have been if they had been based on direct evidence.

Soon after Harvey returned to England he was made a Fellow of the Royal College of Physicians of London, and was then appointed to the staff of St. Bartholomew's Hospital. He settled down to practise, but he must have devoted all the time he could spare to his experiments, for his manuscript notes on these, which are in the British Museum, show that he dissected in these years some eighty different species of animals, in order to learn more about the action of the heart and the blood. He found the cold-blooded animals, fish, frogs and serpents, of particular value for this purpose; for the hearts of such creatures can be exposed, still beating, after they are otherwise dead, and the slowness of the beat enables its course to be followed readily by the unaided eye. So Harvey was able to watch the contraction of the upper chambers of the heart, or auricles, emptying their contents into the main chambers, or ventricles, and then the contraction of these latter, driving the blood into the aorta and the pulmonary artery; and he described the valves in the heart, and at the openings of the great arteries from its ventricles, keeping the flow of blood always in that direction. You can see this in the diagram below.

Harvey observed that when arteries were tied they became empty on the side of the ligature remote from the heart; and he showed how Fabricius's valves in the veins kept the flow in these vessels always towards the heart and away from the rest of the body. And then, from the amount

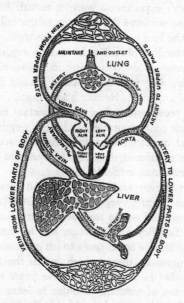

THE BLOOD SYSTEM ACCORDING TO HARVEY

of blood ejected at each beat, and the number of beats in a minute, he calculated that the heart would be bound to deliver into the arteries, in the space of half an hour, more than the whole of the blood in the body. This, he argued, could not be replaced from the juices of the food in that time; and, in any case, the arteries would soon burst and the veins be quickly emptied, unless the blood could somehow find its way through the tissues, from the arteries into the veins, and so back to the heart. 'I began to think,' he writes, 'whether there might not be a motion, as it were in a

circle.' He showed, indeed, that there was a double circuit
—from the right side of the heart to the lungs and back
from these to the left side, and then from this to the rest of
the body and back again to the right side. And so by systematic experiment he found the solution which, as we have
seen, Cesalpino and the others had earlier begun to approach by mere reasoning and argument. I think that Sir
Michael Foster, in his book on *The History of Physiology*,
rightly maintains that Harvey's great merit was not merely
to have made the discovery of the circulation, to which
others had come so near in theory, but to have demonstrated it and established it for all time by his triumphant
use of the experimental method.

Harvey's work did not complete the story. He had made
it certain that the blood passed from the finest visible
branches of the arteries to the finest visible branches of the
veins, and so back to the heart; but he could not, with his
unaided vision, discover how it did so. Knowledge of that
had to wait till Malpighi, with his microscope, was able to
see and to describe the network of fine capillary vessels
which intervene and provide the connexion. Nor did Harvey understand what happens to the blood as it passes
through this capillary network in the lungs; though he did
refer to his intention to write another book, about the respiration. He might, one thinks, have gone much further if
his activities had not been interrupted by the Civil War;
for, though he did not take sides, he was suspect as physician to King Charles, and a large part of his great collection
of notes was destroyed. But he had given the first great
demonstration of what the experimental method could do,
and, though he died three years before the Royal Society
began, younger men who must all have known him—Boyle,
Hooke, Mayow, Lower, Christopher Wren—were there to
carry on the great tradition, and, in following it, to found
the experimental sciences of chemistry and physics. And
among Harvey's bequests to the Royal College of Physicians
was one providing for an annual oration, still delivered every
year, in which the Fellows were to be exhorted 'to search
and to study out the secrets of nature by way of experiment'.

VI

THE DEVELOPMENT OF
SCIENTIFIC INSTRUMENTS
IN THE SEVENTEENTH
CENTURY

S. Lilley, M.SC., PH.D.

*Sometime Fellow of St. John's College, Cambridge
Resident Tutor, Extra-Mural Department,
University of Birmingham*

IF you look around any research laboratory nowadays you cannot help noticing that it is full of apparatus and instruments specially made for scientific work, things that you would not expect to find anywhere outside a laboratory. But if you had visited a scientist's workroom in the Middle Ages you would have found very few instruments indeed. Of course, there were variations between one science and another, and between one man and another. But you would quite often find a man who would have called himself a scientist (if the term had been used then) and yet whose workroom contained no more apparatus than books, paper, pen and ink—he thought you could investigate nature by *thinking* about it.

The change from only thinking about things to investigating them experimentally with special apparatus is one of the chief changes that gave rise to modern science. It is a change that took place mainly in the seventeenth century, though you can see trends in the sixteenth century that lead up to it.

Today most of the apparatus in a physics laboratory has been specially designed and made for scientific purposes. But that was not true of the early days of the Scientific Revolution. Visiting the laboratory of a really go-ahead scientist in the late sixteenth or early seventeenth century, you would find far more instruments than a hundred years earlier. But they would not be specially built scientific instruments in the main. They would be mostly instruments which the scientist had found it convenient to borrow from other walks of life. You might find some of the surveying and measuring instruments that the land surveyors used, or a goldsmith's balance, carpenter's tools and measuring instruments, and so on. And most likely of all, you would find some instruments borrowed from navigation —for navigation was going ahead so fast then that it had produced quite a number of instruments that were very refined judged by previous standards.

Take the case of William Gilbert, whose book *On the Magnet*, published in 1600, was the beginning of modern magnetic science—it was more than that: it was the first book written by an academically trained scholar for scholars to read which used a thoroughly experimental approach. His main instruments were navigational instruments—above all the ship's compass—or very simple modifications of them. But he also gives us a glimpse of what was to come, in the form of a few important instruments which he made specially for scientific purposes. One was his *terrella*, or 'little earth'—a model of the spherical earth, cut out of magnetic material. He was able to show that magnets brought near his 'little earth' behaved very much in the same way as the compass does at the surface of the real earth. And so with this specially designed apparatus he went some way towards explaining the earth's magnetism.

That, then, was the situation in the early days of the Scientific Revolution—most instruments borrowed from the practical crafts, but once in a while an instrument specially made for scientific purposes. On the other hand, after the middle of the seventeenth century, if you had again visited a go-ahead scientist, you would have found lots of instruments designed specially for scientific purposes. So the big development in scientific instruments happened between 1600 and, say, 1660 or 1670. Let us follow the evolution of one of the most important of the new instruments—the air-pump.

The story starts outside science. In the sixteenth century there had been remarkable developments in industry —most remarkable of all in mining. Mining was a rapidly growing industry, and mines were getting bigger and deeper. As they grew deeper it became more and more difficult to protect them from flooding. To deal with this problem, miners gave a great deal of attention to improving and developing pumps. The growth of towns requiring artificial water supplies also brought pumps to the fore. Many types of pumps were used, but the one that interests us now is the ordinary suction-pump—the type that you still often see as the village pump, working 'by suction' (as we say in everyday language) from above. Pumps had formerly been rather rare things; now they became fairly common. Some scientists became interested in pumps because they wanted to improve them, to help solve mine drainage or water supply problems. Others did not have that direct practical interest; but looking around them they were bound to see plenty of pumps, watch how they worked, and wonder why they sometimes failed to work. And it is one of the characteristics of a good scientist that he can see scientific problems or scientific opportunities in the things that he meets in ordinary life. Pumps soon suggested scientific ideas to men with really watchful minds.

Pumps played a big part in seventeenth-century science. In the last chapter you heard about William Harvey and the circulation of the blood. A big part of his inspiration was the idea of thinking of the heart as a pump. Or again, some of you may know the story of Galileo and the pump —how some thinking that he did about why a certain pump wouldn't work properly led eventually to an understanding of atmospheric pressure and the invention of the barometer. You can find that story in the book by Conant listed in the Bibliography at the end of this book.

So far we have been talking about water-pumps. But some time between 1635 and 1654 a certain Otto von

Guericke, Mayor of Magdeburg, had a brilliant idea. He was essentially a practical man—he had been a military engineer and fortification expert during the Thirty Years War. But if he was a practical man, he was one with a vision that went far beyond immediate practice. He conceived the idea of using a suction-pump, not to suck up water, but to suck the *air* out of some vessel, so that one could see what happens. His apparatus was crude, but it produced some pretty startling results. He took two hollow bronze hemispheres, fitting edge to edge to form a sphere, and used his air-pump to draw out the air from between them. He then showed that two teams of eight horses harnessed to the two hemispheres and pulling in opposite directions could not pull them apart. There was a demonstration on a colossal scale of the terrific force of atmospheric pressure! Guericke also tried the experiment of weighing a hollow sphere in its normal state and again when all the air was taken out, and so got a rough idea of the weight of air.

Guericke's contribution to the development of the air-pump was important, but he can hardly be called a genius. The instrument as he developed it was not capable of very much more than the half-dozen or so experiments that he did with it. It was left to the Honourable Robert Boyle, a first-class genius, to see what really could be got out of the air-pump. His idea was to make it in such a way that you could put various objects into the receiver—as he called the vessel from which the air was pumped out—and see how they were affected by being deprived of air. In the picture of his second air-pump which appears on page 46 the receiver is on the right. It was made of glass so that he could see what happened to anything inside when the air was pumped out. And there were various ingenious devices for manipulating from outside the things that were inside without letting in the air. Boyle's first set of air-pump experiments were done in the years 1658 and 1659, and published in 1660; and he continued the work from time to time up to 1679. Boyle, like many scientists of his time, was fortified in his love of science by a strong belief that it would produce important practical benefits. And in his

book he tells us that his chief object in this work was to get
a better understanding of respiration and so, perhaps, to
bring improvements to men's health. At the same time, if
you read the book you soon come to realise that although
this hope of application was important to him, it often re-
ceded far into the background, and he just found himself
led from one thing to another by the sheer love of doing
the experiments and discovering new things. Essentially,
Boyle's method was to put anything that he happened to
think of into the receiver, pump out the air and see what
happened.

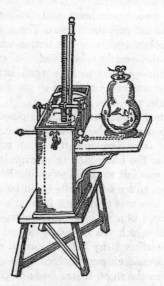

BOYLE'S SECOND AIR-PUMP

He hung a watch in the receiver by a fine thread. While
the air was still there he could hear it ticking distinctly.
Then he pumped out the air. The ticking gradually faded
and eventually nothing could be heard, although he could
see that the watch was still going. You see what that leads
to? Sound needs air to carry it; in fact, as we now know,

sound is carried by waves in air. If the air is removed there will be no sound. Did you notice that I said Boyle could still *see* the watch going? All his experiments depended on the fact that he could *see* what was going on—in other words, light still comes from the object to the eye even when the air is removed. As a matter of fact that point was so obvious that Boyle hardly took any notice of it. But still the distinction did emerge from his work—and was very important for the future of science—that sound is carried by air, while light is not—light is quite independent of air. In fact a great many of Boyle's experiments served to distinguish natural phenomena into two great classes—those which depend on the presence of air (like sound), and those which do not (like light). He found, for example, that magnetic attraction is independent of the presence of air.

Again, he put various burning things in the receiver—a lighted candle, burning charcoal, and so on—and he found that when the air was pumped out the fire was extinguished. In other words, combustion—burning—depends in some way on the presence of air. Then he tried putting small birds and animals in the receiver—the picture on page 46 shows a mouse in it. When the air was pumped out these creatures found difficulty in breathing and they soon died. So air, he had proved, is essential to respiration and to life. Now he put these last two experiments together: burning depends on air, and breathing also depends on air; does it not seem likely that there is something in common between the two, that respiration and combustion are essentially the same process? Boyle put out that suggestion cautiously, but we now know that he was quite right. In burning, the thing that burns combines with oxygen from the air. And in respiration the oxygen from the air is carried by the blood from the lungs to different parts of the body, where it combines with other substances in a way that is essentially slow combustion. It took over a hundred years to make this clear, but Boyle had taken the first big step.

There are many parts of Boyle's air-pump that I have not been able to touch on. One important result that arose from it, though rather indirectly, was the discovery of the relation which we now call Boyle's Law—that the pressure and volume of a gas are inversely proportional—which those of you who have studied physics will know about.

Now, of course, the air-pump was only one of many new pieces of apparatus invented in the seventeenth century. The telescope was another. The origin of the telescope is rather obscure, but it was Galileo in 1609 who realised and demonstrated its value as a scientific instrument, instead of a mere toy or a military device. With the aid of the telescope Galileo discovered that Jupiter had moons circling round it. In an earlier chapter Professor Dingle explained how important this discovery was for establishing the Copernican theory that the earth and planets move round the sun. In Copernicus's time and for centuries after, there was no direct evidence for Copernicus's theory. The arguments in its favour were merely that it explained things more simply and made calculations easier. Now Galileo saw the moons revolving round Jupiter, and it struck him that here was a miniature demonstration of the Copernican theory. Arguing by analogy, it made Copernicus's theory seem more likely.

Galileo also discovered that the Milky Way is really myriads of stars which the unaided eye could not distinguish from one another. He saw sunspots, and thereby helped to kill the old belief that the heavens were perfect and made of different stuff from this imperfect earth. He found the mountains on the moon and by measuring their shadows got a rough estimate of their height. And that was only a beginning; during the rest of the century the telescope revolutionised astronomy.

Now the air-pump and the telescope were just two of the many new scientific instruments that appeared in the seventeenth century—the microscope, the thermometer, the barometer, the pendulum clock, and many others ranging down to various detailed improvements in measuring instruments. So what you have got to do is to think of all the new discoveries that came from the air-pump and telescope (and I only mentioned a few of them) and then think that ten or twenty other instruments each produced just as many startling discoveries. And then you will begin to realise that a very large part of that rapid progress which science made in the seventeenth century—and ever since—was due to the invention of scientific instruments. That is putting it too mildly. The progress was due to the fact that, after centuries of simply thinking about things or doing the very simplest experiments, scientists had at last come to realise that in many branches of their work the real way to discover the truth about nature was to do experiments with the help of instruments specially thought out and constructed for the purpose.

That would be the first general conclusion to remember —that in the seventeenth century scientific instruments were used on a really big scale for the first time in all history, and the use of them suddenly opened up vast new fields of discovery. But it did more than merely lead to new discoveries. It played a major part in establishing the *experimental method*—the method that characterises modern science. Without special instruments you can do a few experiments. But they don't really get you very far—not far enough to show clearly that experiment is a better method than the old method of just thinking about things. Then, when the new instruments came along, experiment produced such remarkable results that it only took a few decades to demonstrate that the experimental method is better than any other.

Again, the points we discussed tell us something about the way science is affected by the rest of life. The air-pump, you will remember, was derived from the suction-pump that had been made common by advances in mining. In a world where there were not lots of ordinary suction-pumps it would be theoretically possible to invent an air-pump—but it wouldn't be likely to happen. So that we can reasonably say that the air-pump was only possible because of developments in the mining industry. Of course scientific instruments are not often (and nowadays not usually) derived so directly from the machines and instruments of industry. But at least they only become possible when industry has reached a sufficiently advanced level to be able to construct them. To make that clear you would have to go into far more detail. But if, for example, you were to read Boyle's air-pump books right through, you would find that many of his experiments depended on getting apparatus built by the very best craftsmen, using the most advanced craft technique available. A century earlier they would not have been technically possible. And every now and then Boyle had to confess that he could not do an experiment he had thought of, because he could not find workmen capable of making the apparatus accurately enough.

And that brings me to another point. At all periods in history there have been crafts and craftsmen who could have provided ideas for scientific apparatus—not such good apparatus as in the seventeenth century, but still better than the scientists actually used. But in fact various forms of snobbery prevented the scientist from learning anything from humble workmen. The practical things that craftsmen did were regarded as beneath the notice of scholars. And so craftsmen's instruments did not get into the scientist's study. One of the big things about the sixteenth and seventeenth centuries was that this snobbery began to disappear, and so scientists like Gilbert, Galileo, Guericke and Boyle became willing to learn what they could from the craftsmen and to take over craftsmen's apparatus to make scientific instruments. Gilbert got apparatus from sea captains and the makers of marine instruments. Galileo opened his greatest book by saying that he learned much from the skilled workers of the Arsenal at Venice. Boyle was always preaching how much the scientists could learn from the craftsman (as well as how much the crafts could be improved by science). These men of the seventeenth century took craft knowledge and craft experience and craft skill and craftsmen's instruments and combined them with their own systematic theoretical training. And out of this combination they produced scientific instruments and experimental science as we know it. There is no space now to discuss why seventeenth-century scientists took this new attitude of not being snobbish about their work. I can only drop the hint that it is closely connected with the rising importance of industry and the growing influence of men who gained a living from industry and commerce, as against the old aristocracy who simply lived by owning land.

VII

NEWTON AND

HIS UNIVERSE

Herbert Butterfield

*Professor of Modern History
in the University of Cambridge*

VARIOUS aspects of the Scientific Revolution have now
been illustrated and we have examined the changes
that were taking place both in scientific method and in
modes of thought in the seventeenth century. The climax
of the story comes with Sir Isaac Newton in the last quarter
of that century. In this period the new methods really come
to prevail, and a completely different scheme or diagram
of the universe is achieved.

A host of scientists, especially in London and in Paris in
the 1670's and 1680's, show that a new era has been born
and has created great exhilaration—a tremendous fermentation—in people's minds. The English Royal Society and
the French Academy of Sciences were entering upon their
distinguished careers; there was more collaboration and
communication between the scientists, by the development
of periodical literature for example, so that discoveries were
generally soon known, or discussions were held or knowledge was exchanged. Also the scientific societies proved
better able to bear the expense of experimental work than
the private individual had been in the past. We have
evidence of the social success of the sciences in these decades, especially in the France of Louis XIV; and we see
how crowds—sometimes nobles and distinguished people,
sometimes foreigners—would flock to lectures and demon-

strations, and there was a great rage for the new ideas and new fashions of thought that were coming in. We even see a great attempt to popularise science, and one French writer, Fontenelle, set out to make science as easy for ladies to read as the latest novel.

To understand the situation it is necessary that we should cast our eyes over the period of almost exactly a century that led up to Sir Isaac Newton, and we must note certain developments taking place in that period—developments which form the main ribs in the framework of the Scientific Revolution itself. It is useful to remember that Sir Isaac Newton comes to crown a great process of scientific development, and gathers up the achievements of many predecessors, though he combines them into something entirely new. We must note in the first place that Copernicus himself did not produce a satisfactory picture or explanation of what was happening in the skies, and did not scientifically establish his case. The controversy concerning the rotation of the earth did not become even very intense until the close of the sixteenth century, nearly sixty years after his death. Even then the thing which greatly agitated the world was not Copernicus's theory itself but a number of disturbing new discoveries that were made in the sky in that period. The first occurred in 1572, and it was the appearance of a new star—one which shone with particular brightness and then disappeared two years later—a thing which ought to have been impossible, since the skies and the heavenly bodies were supposed to be incapable of change, incapable of either generation or corruption. Then in 1577 a new comet appeared, and as methods of observation had been much improved even since the time of Copernicus, it became impossible to go on believing the old theory that comets existed only under the moon—because this comet was seen to range through the higher skies and actually cut a path through that series of crystal spheres which had been supposed to be impenetrable.

Before this time men had gone on believing that comets were really terrestrial things—exhalations or fumes from the earth which became ignited in the upper atmosphere. Now, however, the comet was proved to be a celestial phenomenon, and it showed that strange irregularities were liable to occur in the skies. Even men who could not swallow the Copernican theory began to believe that the older theory of the universe must have been wrong, at any rate in parts; and some of them, even though they were conservative-minded, began to realise that the crystal spheres, one above the other, could not exist in reality, and that the sun, the stars and the planets must be floating, unattached to anything, in a wilderness of empty space. There was a demand for a general 'renovation of astronomy' as it was called, a fresh overhauling of the whole matter. This general spring-cleaning in astronomy was a work that depended on revising and correcting one's observation of the skies, and in this it differed from the Copernican attempt to form a system—much of it was due in fact to a Danish astronomer, Tycho Brahe, who did not believe in the Copernican theory at all, but who brought the careful observation of the skies to perhaps the greatest perfection possible before the invention of the telescope. He put forward a compromise theory, half-way between the Copernican and the more ancient one, and in the seventeenth century this theory became somewhat fashionable in its various modified forms. According to this view some of the planets did go round the sun, as Copernicus had said, but still the sun and this miniature solar system revolved with the rest of the planets around the motionless earth.

All the same, if the heavenly bodies were rolling round in the ocean of empty space, it was difficult to imagine what could keep them in position and hold them to their appointed course; and some people inclined to the view of an interesting English experimenter, William Gilbert, who thought that the earth was a species of magnet, and that magnetism held the heavenly bodies in their places, so that the idea of 'attraction' was introduced into the argument. More intellectual disturbance was caused by Galileo, who with his telescope discovered the spots on the sun and showed that the heavenly bodies could not be made of pure and immaculate material after all. But when Galileo argued that the tides were a proof of the motion of the earth—

that the oceans rose and fell because of the shaking of the vessel which held them—he did not convince the world.

So far as the particular science of astronomy was concerned, all these various changes put men's minds into a turmoil, and any individual made his choice of his picture and theory of the universe. But, apart from all this, much work was being done, especially in the first thirty years of the seventeenth century, on a different matter, in a widely different realm, namely on the general problem of motion. All this was to have great importance for the study of the skies, because it was necessary to show why the heavenly bodies kept in motion, and the chief obstruction to the Copernican theory lay in the difficulty of imagining what could make this ponderous earth go round. Galileo is particularly important in this study of motion, because he almost completed a development which had been taking place towards what we call the modern doctrine of inertia. He saw that if a body is once in motion we do not have to look for things to explain why it should continue in motion —it will continue that motion until something intervenes to stop it or slacken it or hasten it or deflect it. In other words, we are really faced with something that has to be explained if the motion of the body ceases or is changed in any way. A little later Descartes completed the statement of this modern law of inertia by showing clearly that the body tends to continue its motion indefinitely in a straight line.

It was essential to have this new doctrine, because the older teaching made it impossible to give a rational explanation of the way in which projectiles move. If—as men believed down to this period—any body which was in motion had to have a mover pushing or pulling it all the time, there was no plausible way of explaining why an arrow should go on at all after it had lost its initial contact with its bow-string, or why a cannon ball should ever leave the cannon's mouth. Everything became much more easy once it was seen that a body in motion tended simply to continue in motion along a straight line until something interfered with it. The principle, however, would explain why a body flies off at a tangent, but it would not explain the constant movement of the heavenly bodies—the planets, for example, which a famous astronomer and mathematician, Kepler, had shown to move in elliptical orbits around the sun.

Somewhat unconsciously, men were developing a tendency to believe that if you could explain motion on the earth, this would help to explain also the movements in the sky. In other words, they were tending to depart from the older view that everything in the heavens was composed of a special kind of matter subject to its own peculiar laws. The foundation of the new science of dynamics, therefore, was bound to be of importance for the development of the new astronomy. This was realised by Galileo, who tried to dove-tail these two sciences into one another—he tried to explain earthly movements and heavenly movements by the same laws. Galileo also helped to remove one of the obstructions to the idea of the rotation of the earth by the brilliant way in which he expounded (though he did not exactly invent) the argument that if the earth rotated everything on the surface, including the air, would rotate with it, and so would leave one with the impression of being at rest; just as everything moves together in the cabin of a moving ship, in such a way that you imagine it to be still. This argument showed how it might be possible that the earth should be in motion though the fact might not be apparent, but it did not prove that it was the earth rather than the sun which moved.

While these things were happening, further developments were taking place in quite a different branch of scientific thought, though people did not realise the importance that this was going to have in future for the explanation of the problem of the skies. The field in question related to the problem of gravitation; and it will be remembered that on the older theory, which went back to Aristotle, things had weight and tended to fall because they aspired to rush to the centre of the universe, which happened to be the centre of the earth. On this view, if you were to take a handful of mud on to the planet Mars, it would tend to fall to the earth, the heavenly bodies being composed of material without weight or gravity. Such a view could not be held any longer if the earth moved round the sun—because the earth would no longer be the centre of the universe, and gravity was supposed to be the tendency to move to the centre of the universe. We find the view being put forward, therefore, at one moment that the sun and the moon, as well as the earth, are able to exert gravity, each acting as an independent centre. Copernicus said that things would be drawn to the sun or the moon or the earth because in everything there was the tendency for matter to assemble into spheres. Early in the seventeenth century gravity was held to be something like a case of magnetic attraction, the greater mass attracting the smaller with a power which was thought to vary in some degree according to distance. Later again, we find the view being put forward that gravity varied inversely as the square of the distance, though this discovery was not widely accepted or even widely known for some time. Somebody also put forward the view that gravity did not merely operate in the sun or the moon or the earth, but was a relationship existing between all particles of matter, an attraction that the various parts of matter exerted on one another. It will be noticed that instead of regarding the apple as having a disposition which induced it to yearn to be at the centre of the earth, men are now beginning to reverse the picture and say that it is the earth which exerts a pull on the apple; all of which makes it clear that a different attitude was being adopted to the problem of gravitation. Somebody suggested—a very modern view—that the moon would fly off at a tangent, right away from the earth, if it was not kept in place by the pull of the earth's gravity upon it.

So there were various theories put forward in the seventeenth century, first of all concerning the motion of the heavenly bodies, and secondly concerning the motion of terrestrial bodies, and thirdly concerning the principle of gravitation. One set of views existed in one man's head, another in another man's head, and the person who had hit on the truth about gravitation would have a false idea of the principles of motion, and nobody had picked out the right theory from all of the sets of ideas. Nobody had realised that when the correct ones had been adopted in each case they might be neatly dove-tailed into one another to form a coherent system. There was even a further independent branch of scientific thought that was to have its place in the jig-saw puzzle. The world had long been mystified by circular motion, and by what we call centrifugal force; and even the great Galileo had been defective on this subject. But in 1659 a famous scientist, Huygens, analysed the matter, and found the formula for the pull which a stone exerts when it is swung round in a sling—the force that has to be exerted by the sling to prevent the stone from flying off at a tangent. That was to be an essential factor in the ultimate solution of the problem. It was another item that would help to form a single interlocking system if it should ever occur to anybody to put it with others which I have mentioned and dove-tail the various parts.

Sir Isaac Newton was a young man and had hardly ceased to be an undergraduate when, in 1665–66, he had the brilliant idea of selecting the right conjecture in the case of each of the problems I have mentioned, and then dove-tailing them together to show that they fitted into one another. He accepted the view that the heavenly bodies were floating in space, and that both they and all other particles of matter exerted an attraction on one another, an attraction dependent on their relative mass, and varying inversely with the square of the distance between them. He accepted the modern principle of inertia, and applied it to the planets which tended to maintain their existing motion in a straight line, but which were held in by the pull of gravity so that they were curved round into their elliptical orbits, just as a cannon ball fired into the air is pulled in a curve back to the earth by the effect of its own gravity. He imagined that the moon was like a stone in a sling, tending to fly off at a tangent, but held in by the force of gravity; and he worked out that the 'pull' which was necessary to hold the moon in its course was the equivalent of gravitation—mathematically equivalent to the force which actually draws the apple to the ground. In fact, the same force was tugging at the moon—taking due account of relative weights and distances—as drew the apple down from the branch of a tree.

Newton showed mathematically that if the forces operated in the way that I have said, the planets would describe just the kind of ellipse round the sun which Kepler had shown that they actually followed. For various reasons he was not satisfied with his original calculations, however, and kept them for twenty years, until he had settled certain doubts. By this time, moreover, new observations had rectified certain measurements in the earth and the sky. Newton's results were finally published in the *Principia* in 1687, and they formed the climax of the Scientific Revolution, at a time when, as we have already seen, so many scientists were doing brilliant things in London and in Paris. In the case of some of the ideas which Isaac Newton assembled together to form his system, he had to discover them over again, because, though they might have been discovered before he set to work, they were not generally known. In some cases—the mathematical formulas relating to centrifugal force and to gravity, for example—the results had previously been found but had not hitherto been published. Furthermore, in the case of the work of both Newton and some of his predecessors, it proved to be the case that the scientists themselves on occasion would have found their progress barred unless there had been at various stages remarkable improvements in mathematics. Newton himself actually was responsible for some of the important developments in this field.

So Newton produced a kind of clockwork universe, in which the whole system seemed automatic once God had, so to speak, wound up the spring or set the machinery in motion. Now, for the first time, it was possible to form a coherent system of the universe on the theory that the earth might be in motion. Now it was possible to explain how such a solid earth could keep in motion at all. Unlike the ancient system, moreover, Newton's theory enabled all the motions in earth and sky to be reduced to the same formulas and connected with the same laws, so that the whole universe seemed to be subject to one unifying system of law. That system convinced men—indeed the whole mechanistic trend of the seventeenth-century scientific movement produced the result—that the mechanical explanations were

the things to look for, even in subjects like biology where
we now know that purely mechanical explanations are in-
sufficient. Because of the repercussions that Newton's *Principia* had on many aspects of human thought, we must
regard the year 1687 as a most important date in the history of civilisation. Some of these repercussions will be
discussed later.

VIII

HOW THE SCIENTIFIC REVOLUTION OF THE SEVENTEENTH CENTURY AFFECTED OTHER BRANCHES OF THOUGHT

Basil Willey

*King Edward VII Professor of English Literature
in the University of Cambridge*

I N order to get a bird's-eye view of any century it is quite useful to imagine it as a stretch of country, or a landscape, which we are looking at from a great height, let us say from an aeroplane. If we view the seventeenth century in this way we shall be struck immediately by the great contrast between the scenery and even the climate of its earlier and that of its later years. At first we get mountain ranges, torrents, and all the picturesque interplay of alternating storm and brightness; then, further on, the land slopes down to a richly cultivated plain, broken for a while by outlying heights and spurs, but finally becoming level country, watered by broad rivers, adorned with parks and mansions, and lit up by steady sunshine. The mountains connect backwards with the central medieval Alps, and the plain leads forwards with little break into our own times. To drop the metaphor before it begins to be misleading, we may say that the seventeenth century was an age of transition, and although every century can be so described, the seventeenth deserves this label better than most, because it lies between the Middle Ages and the modern world. It witnessed one of the greatest changes which have ever taken place in men's ways of thinking about the world they live in.

I happen to be interested in literature, amongst other things, and when I turn to this century I cannot help noticing that it begins with Shakespeare and Donne, leads on to Milton, and ends with Dryden and Swift: that is to say, it begins with a literature full of passion, paradox, imagination, curiosity and complexity, and ends with one distinguished rather by clarity, precision, good sense and definiteness of statement. The end of the century is the beginning of what has been called the Age of Prose and Reason, and we may say that by then the qualities necessary for good prose had got the upper hand over those which produce the greatest kinds of poetry. But that is not all: we find the same sort of thing going on elsewhere. Take architecture, for example; you all know the style of building called Elizabethan or Jacobean—it is quaint and fanciful, sometimes rugged in outline, and richly ornamented with carving and decoration in which Gothic and classical ingredients are often mixed up together. Well, by the end of the century this has given place to the style of Christopher Wren and the so-called Queen Anne architects, which is plain, well proportioned, severe, and purely classical without Gothic trimmings. And here there is an important point to notice: it is true that the seventeenth century begins with a blend of medieval and modern elements, and ends with the triumph of the modern; but observe that in those days to be 'modern' often meant to be 'classical', that is, to imitate the Greeks and Romans. We call the age of Dryden, Pope and Addison the 'Augustan' Age, and the men of that time really felt that they were living in an epoch like that of the Emperor Augustus—an age of enlightenment, learning and true civilisation—and congratulated themselves on having escaped from the errors and superstitions of the dark and monkish Middle Ages. To write and build and think like the ancients meant that you were rea-

sonable beings, cultivated and urbane—that you had abandoned the shadow of the cloister for the cheerful light of
the market place or the coffee house. If you were a scientist
(or 'natural philosopher') you had to begin, it is true, by
rejecting many ancient theories, particularly those of Aristotle, but you knew all the while that by thinking independently and taking nothing on trust you were following
the ancients in spirit though not in letter.

Or let us glance briefly at two other spheres of interest:
politics and religion, beginning with politics. Here again
you notice that the century begins with Cavalier and
Roundhead and ends with Tory and Whig—that is to say,
it begins with a division arousing the deepest passions and
prejudices, not to be settled without bloodshed, and ends
with the mere opposition of two political parties, differing
in principle of course, but socially at one, and more ready
to alternate peaceably with each other. The Hanoverians
succeed the Stuarts, and what more need be said? The
divine right of kings is little more heard of, and the scene
is set for prosaic but peaceful development. Similarly in religion, the period opens with the long and bitter struggle
between Puritan and Anglican, continuing through civil
war, and accompanied by fanaticism, persecution and exile,
and by the multiplication of hostile sects; it ends with the
Toleration Act, and with the comparatively mild dispute
between the Deists and their opponents as to whether
Nature was not after all a clearer evidence of God than
Scripture, and the conscience a safer guide than the creeds.
In short, wherever you turn you find the same tale repeated
in varying forms: the ghosts of history are being laid; dark-
ness and tempest are yielding to the light of common day.
Major issues have been settled or shelved, and men begin
to think more about how to live together in concord and
prosperity.

Merely to glance at this historical landscape is enough
to make one seek some explanation of these changes. If the
developments had conflicted with each other we might
have put them down to a number of different causes, but
since they all seem to be setting in one direction it is natural to suppose that they were all due to one common

underlying cause. There are various ways of accounting for historical changes: some people believe, for instance, that economic causes are at the bottom of everything, and that the way men earn their living, and the way in which wealth is produced and distributed, determine how men think and write and worship. Others believe that ideas, rather than material conditions, are what control history, and that the important question to ask about any period is what men then believed to be true, what their philosophy and religion were like. There is something to be said on both sides, but we are concerned with a simpler question. We know that the greatest intellectual change in modern history was completed during the seventeenth century: was that change of such a kind as to explain all those parallel movements we have mentioned? Would it have helped or hindered that drift towards prose and reason, towards classicism, enlightenment and toleration? The great intellectual change was that known as the Scientific Revolution, and I think the answer to these questions is—Yes.

It is not for me to describe that revolution, or to discuss the great discoveries which produced it. My task is only to consider some of the effects it had upon men's thoughts, imaginations and feelings, and consequently upon their ways of expressing themselves. The discoveries—I am thinking mainly of the Copernican astronomy and the laws of motion as explored by Galileo and fully formulated by Newton—shocked men into realising that things were not as they had always seemed, and that the world they were living in was really quite different from what they had been taught to suppose. When the crystal spheres of the old world-picture were shattered, and the earth was shown to be one of many planets rolling through space, it was not everyone who greeted this revelation with enthusiasm as Giordano Bruno did. Many felt lost and confused, because the old picture had not only seemed obviously true to common sense, but was confirmed by Scripture and by Aristotle, and hallowed by the age-long approval of the Church. What Matthew Arnold said about the situation in the nineteenth century applies also to the seventeenth: religion had attached its emotion to certain supposed facts, and now the facts were failing it. You can hear this note of loss in Donne's well-known lines:

> And new philosophy calls all in doubt;
> The element of fire is quite put out;
> The sun is lost, and th' earth, and no man's wit
> Can well direct him where to look for it.

Not only 'the element of fire', but the very distinction between heaven and earth had vanished—the distinction, I mean, between the perfect and incorruptible celestial bodies from the moon upwards, and the imperfect and corruptible terrestrial bodies below it. New stars had appeared, which showed that the heavens could change, and the telescope revealed irregularities in the moon's surface—that is, the moon was not a perfect sphere, as a celestial body should be. So Sir Thomas Browne could write:

> 'While we look for incorruption in the heavens, we find they are but like the earth;—durable in their main bodies, alterable in their parts; whereof, besides comets and new stars, perspectives (i.e. telescopes) begin to tell tales, and the spots that wander about the sun, with Phaeton's favour, would make clear conviction.'

Naturally it took a long time for these new ideas to sink in, and Milton still treats the old and the new astronomies as equally acceptable alternatives. The Copernican scheme, however, was generally accepted by the second half of the century. By that time the laws governing the motion of bodies on earth had also been discovered, and finally it was revealed by Newton that the law whereby an apple falls to the ground is the very same as that which keeps the planets in their courses. The realisation of this vast unifying idea meant a complete re-focusing of men's ideas about God, Nature and Man, and the relationships between them. The whole cosmic movement, in the heavens and on earth, must now be ascribed no longer to a divine pressure acting through the Primum Mobile, and angelic intelligences controlling the spheres, but to a gravitational pull which could be mathematically calculated. The universe turned out to be a Great Machine, made up of material parts which all moved through space and time according to the strictest rules of mechanical causation. That is to say, since every effect in nature had a physical cause, no room or need was left for supernatural agencies, whether divine or diabolical; every phenomenon was explicable in terms of matter and motion, and could be mathematically accounted for or predicted. As Sir James Jeans has said: 'Only after much study did the great principle of causation emerge. In time it was found to dominate the whole of inanimate nature. . . . The final establishment of this law . . . was the triumph of the seventeenth century, the great century of Galileo and Newton.' It is true that mathematical physics had not yet conquered every field: even chemistry was not yet reduced to exactitude, and still less biology and psychology. But Newton said: 'Would that the rest of the phenomena of nature could be deduced by a like kind of reasoning from mechanical principles'—and he believed that they could and would.

I referred just now to some of the immediate effects of the 'New Philosophy' (as it was called); let me conclude by hinting at a few of its ultimate effects. First, it produced a distrust of all tradition, a determination to accept nothing as true merely on authority, but only after experiment and verification. You find Bacon rejecting the philosophy of the medieval Schoolmen, Browne writing a long exposure of popular errors and superstitions (such as the belief that a toad had a jewel in its head, or that an elephant had no joints in its legs), Descartes resolving to doubt everything —even his own senses—until he can come upon something clear and certain, which he finally finds in the fact of his own existence as a thinking being. Thus the chief intellectual task of the seventeenth century became the winnowing of truth from error, fact from fiction or fable. Gradually a sense of confidence, and even exhilaration, set in; the universe seemed no longer mysterious or frightening; everything in it was explicable and comprehensible. Comets and eclipses were no longer dreaded as portents of disaster; witchcraft was dismissed as an old wives' tale. This new feeling of security is expressed in Pope's epitaph on Newton:

Nature and Nature's laws lay hid in night;
God said, *Let Newton be!* and all was light!

How did all this affect men's religious beliefs? The effect
was very different from that of Darwinism on nineteenth-
century religion. In the seventeenth century it was felt that
science had produced a conclusive demonstration of God,
by showing the evidence of His wisdom and power in the
Creation. True, God came to be thought of rather as an
abstract First Cause than as the personal, ever-present God
of religion; the Great Machine implied the Great Mechanic,
but after making the machine and setting it in motion God
had, as it were, retired from active superintendence, and
left it to run by its own laws without interference. But at a
time when inherited religious sentiment was still very powerful, the idea that you could look up through Nature to
Nature's God seemed to offer an escape from one of the
worst legacies of the past—religious controversy and sec-
tarian intolerance. Religion had been endangered by inner
conflict; what could one believe, when the Churches were
all at daggers drawn? Besides, the secular and rational tem-
per brought in by the new science soon began to undermine
the traditional foundations of belief. If nothing had ever
happened which could not be explained by natural, physical causes, what about the supernatural and miraculous
events recorded in the Bible? This was a disturbing thought,
and even in the seventeenth century there were a few who
began to doubt the literal truth of some of the biblical nar-
ratives. But it was reserved for the eighteenth century to
make an open attack upon the miraculous elements in
Christianity, and to compare the Old Testament Jehovah
disparagingly with the 'Supreme Being' or 'First Cause' of
philosophy. For the time, it was possible to feel that science
was pious, because it was simply engaged in studying
God's own handiwork, and because whatever it disclosed
seemed a further proof of His almighty skill as designer of
the universe. Addison exactly expressed this feeling when
he wrote:

The spacious firmament on high,
With all the blue ethereal sky,

> And spangled heavens, a shining frame,
> Their great Original proclaim.
> Th' unwearied Sun from day to day
> Does his Creator's power display;
> And publishes to every land
> The work of an Almighty hand.

Science also gave direct access to God, whereas Church and creed involved you in endless uncertainties and difficulties.

However, some problems and doubts arose to disturb the prevailing optimism. If the universe was a material mechanism, how could Man be fitted into it?—Man, who had always been supposed to have a free will and an immortal soul? Could it be that those were illusions after all? Not many faced up to this, though Hobbes did say that the soul was only a function of the body, and denied the freedom of the will. What was more immediately serious, especially for poetry and religion, was the new tendency to discount all the products of the imagination, and all spiritual insight, as false or fictitious. Everything that was real could be described by mathematical physics as matter in motion, and whatever could not be so described was either unreal or else had not yet been truly explained. Poets and priests had deceived us long enough with vain imaginings; it was now time for the scientists and philosophers to take over, and speak to us, as Sprat says the Royal Society required its members to do, in a 'naked, natural' style, bringing all things as close as possible to the 'mathematical plainness'. Poets might rave, and priests might try to mystify us, but sensible men would ignore them, preferring good sense, and sober, prosaic demonstration. It was said at the time that philosophy (which then included what we call science) had cut the throat of poetry. This does not mean that no more good poetry could then be produced: after all, Dryden and Pope were both excellent poets. But when all has been said they do lack visionary power: their merits are those of their age—sense, wit, brilliance, incisiveness and point. It is worth noticing that when the Romantic movement began a hundred years later, several of the leading poets attacked science for having killed the universe and turned man into a reasoning machine. But no such thoughts worried the men of the Augustan Age; their prevailing feeling was satisfaction at living in a world that was rational through and through, a world that had been explained favourably, explained piously, and explained by an Englishman. The modern belief in progress takes its rise at this time; formerly it had been thought that perfection lay in antiquity, and that subsequent history was one long decline. But now that Bacon, Boyle, Newton and Locke had arisen, who could deny that the ancients had been far surpassed? Man could now hope to control his environment as never before, and who could say what triumphs might not lie ahead? Even if we feel that the victory of science was then won at the expense of some of man's finer faculties, we can freely admit that it brought with it many good gifts as well —tolerance, reasonableness, release from fear and superstition—and we can pardon, and even envy, that age for its temporary self-satisfaction.

IX

THE BIRTH OF
MODERN CHEMISTRY

Douglas McKie, D.SC., PH.D.

*Reader in the History of Science,
University of London*

GREAT advances in astronomy, mechanics and physics were among the first results of the seventeenth-century revolution in scientific thought, as the earlier chapters in this book have shown. The science of chemistry was, however, not set on its modern road until almost the end of the eighteenth century. The reasons for this delay were, first, the ancient and at that time still acceptable theory of the composition of matter, and, second, the more recent theory of combustion that arose in the seventeenth and eighteenth centuries.

The ancient theory of the composition of matter was formulated in Greece and specially developed by Aristotle in the fourth century B.C. It regarded the vast multitude of different substances that we see in the world around us as consisting of compounds in different proportions of only four elements, earth and water, air and fire. A substance, for example, that burned more vigorously than another was therefore supposed to contain a higher proportion of the element of fire; and one that was more fluid than another was similarly supposed to contain a higher proportion of the element of water. There was, of course, during this long period of over two thousand years no chemical proof that earth and water and air and fire were elements, or that Nature's enormous variety of materials was made up of only four primary substances, but the theory helped to explain many facts in ways that were easily understood.

The other cause of delay in the reform of chemistry was a theory of combustion formulated by two German chemists, Becher and Stahl, in the seventeenth and eighteenth centuries, according to which all combustible and inflammable substances were assumed to contain a common principle of inflammability, which Stahl named 'phlogiston', so that, when a combustible substance was burnt, 'phlogiston' was said to have escaped from it in the form of fire and flame. Combustion was therefore a decomposition. It was a reasonable sort of explanation. Most of us today, without our present knowledge built on past discoveries, would be quite ready to agree that, when a match is struck or a candle burns, some 'fire-stuff' is released from each of them—and so likewise for other kinds of burning.

One application of the 'phlogiston' theory was eventually to lead chemists into much confusion and to help to bring about its downfall. It arose in this way. When a metal, such as copper or lead, is heated, it turns into a powdery substance and its metallic properties are lost. (The same thing happens in the familiar rusting of iron, but there without the application of heat.) The chemists of that time explained this by saying that a metal was a kind of combustible and that, when heated, it lost its 'phlogiston', leaving the powdery residue, which they called a calx. They knew that if this calx was heated afresh with charcoal, it was converted back again into metal; and charcoal, since it would burn away almost entirely, was held to be very rich in 'phlogiston'. The heating of the calx with charcoal had therefore restored enough 'phlogiston' to the calx to reconstitute the original metal. Thus a metal was a compound of its calx and 'phlogiston'; and the process of heating a metal to give its calx, called calcination, was a decomposition, a kind of combustion in which 'phlogiston' escaped from the metal.

It was known, on the other hand, that, when a metal was calcined, the weight of the residual calx or powder was greater than the original weight of the metal taken. But how could the weight increase, since something material, namely 'phlogiston', had been lost from the substance of the metal? In answer to this, some of the chemists who accepted the 'phlogiston' theory were driven to suppose that 'phlogiston' did not gravitate as other matter, but levitated—that it naturally rose upwards to the heavens whereas other substances naturally tended to fall to the earth—that it had a negative weight, as we might say. This contradiction was presently to be resolved in a simpler way than by supposing the existence of a kind of matter outside all experience.

So, until the four-element theory and the 'phlogiston' theory were rejected, modern chemistry remained unborn; for earth and air and water and fire are not the elements of which our world is made, and substances do not burn because of the presence in them of a common principle of inflammability or 'fire-stuff'.

The history of the rejection of these theories begins with the discovery of the gases, particularly the discovery of oxygen, which forms one-fifth of the common air. At first it was supposed that gases were mere varieties of common air, changed slightly in properties but still essentially the same. In 1755, however, Joseph Black differentiated one kind of air chemically from common air and gave it the name of 'fixed air'. (It is now known as carbon dioxide.) Black showed that it was produced in the combustion of charcoal, in respiration when air is exhaled from the lungs, and in fermentation. In 1766 Henry Cavendish discovered another air, 'inflammable air', which we now call hydrogen; and from 1772 onwards Joseph Priestley discovered seven other gases, but still described them as 'different kinds of air'.

Joseph Priestley, a Nonconformist minister, was one of the greatest of all chemical experimenters. In August 1774, in one of his most remarkable experiments, made at Bowood House, Calne, Wiltshire, he obtained a new 'air', in which the flame of a candle burned much more brilliantly than in common air; and in March 1775, in studying this new 'air' in further experiments at Lansdowne House, Mayfair, London, he found that it was purer and better than common air for respiration. It was the gas we now call oxygen. Priestley soon suggested that it might be used to increase 'the force of fire' and that 'it might be peculiarly salutary to the lungs in certain morbid cases', two applications that were made later on. He had first used mice to test the respirability of the new 'air' and then he had tried it himself. 'Hitherto,' he wrote, 'only two mice and myself have had the privilege of breathing it.'

In the autumn of 1774 Priestley visited Paris. There he met Antoine Laurent Lavoisier, the founder, indeed the Newton, of modern chemistry. In conversation with Lavoisier, Priestley described his latest discovery—the new 'air' in which the flame of a candle burned much more brilliantly than in common air; and he told Lavoisier that he had obtained it by heating the calx of mercury or the calx of lead.

Lavoisier had long been considering the related problems of combustion and calcination and, as early as 1772, he had concluded that air played an important part in combustion and that the two inflammable substances, phosphorus and sulphur, combined with air when they were burnt and that their weight was increased by this combination with air. Through many months of 1773 he made further experiments; and in 1774–75, after his talk with Priestley, he concluded that the gain in weight of metals on calcination was likewise due to their combination with air; but he still got no further than supposing that it was combination with common air in a pure state, not suspecting at this time that only a part or constituent of the common air was involved.

In 1777, in further experiments, Lavoisier concluded that only a part of the air was involved in combustion, respiration and calcination—the heavier part of the air—and that air itself was not a simple substance but consisted of two 'airs'. One of these was respirable, supported combustion and combined with metals on calcination—it was, he said, the 'salubrious part' of the air; the other part was incapable of supporting combustion or respiration, it was inimical both to fire and life, and it played no part in calcination.

Then, on 3 May 1777, Lavoisier read to the Paris Academy of Sciences an account of one of the most significant of all experiments in the long history of science. It is illustrated below. He heated four ounces of mercury in the vessel A for twelve days and observed that the level of the water* rose in the vessel B, connected as shown with vessel A, and that the rise in level corresponded to a decrease of about one-fifth of the total air contained in the apparatus. The residual air extinguished lighted candles and asphyxiated animals. He then removed the particles of calx of mercury formed in the vessel A by heating and heated them separately in a similar apparatus, collecting the so-called 'air' that they gave off. He had thus obtained from the calx of mercury, which was now reconverted into metallic mercury, the 'air' with which the mercury had

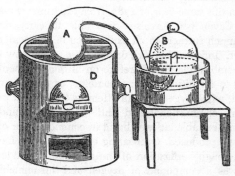

APPARATUS USED BY LAVOISIER WHEN
HE ISOLATED OXYGEN

The neck of the glass vessel A (containing 4 oz. of mercury) was bent to connect with the air in the bell-jar B, inverted over mercury in trough C. After heating for twelve days on the charcoal furnace D, particles of the red calx or oxide of mercury formed in A and the volume of air in the apparatus decreased by about one-fifth. The residual air extinguished a flame and asphyxiated animals. It was nitrogen. Lavoisier then heated the red particles of mercuric oxide in a separate apparatus and collected the gas evolved from them. It amounted to about one-fifth of the original air and it supported combustion and respiration. It was oxygen.

* Mercury in later experiments.

combined in the first part of the experiment. This air was respirable. On mixing it with the air from which it had been removed, he obtained common air once again. He presently gave to this respirable air the name it still bears, oxygen. In this classic experiment, Lavoisier had shown that common air consisted of two 'airs' with strikingly different, indeed opposite, properties; and he had separated them one from the other.

Lavoisier's theory was not at all well received by his contemporaries, who were too much used to the older way of thinking. Even when, in 1783, he began to criticise the 'phlogiston' theory in the light of his own discoveries, he failed to make any serious inroad on the older beliefs.

But in this same year of 1783, from experiments made by Henry Cavendish, Lavoisier was able to carry his new theory much further—to an explanation of the composition of water. 'Inflammable air', or hydrogen as we now call it, was a combustible and therefore on burning it should, according to Lavoisier's theory, combine, as other combustibles did, with oxygen. Yet all attempts to obtain a product from this combustion failed until Cavendish found that, when 'inflammable air' was burnt in common air or oxygen, water was produced. On hearing of this in 1783, Lavoisier made a rough verification of the fact and concluded that water was a compound of oxygen and 'inflammable air', which he later re-named hydrogen (i.e. 'water-former'); and presently he confirmed this by decomposing water into its two constituent gases.

Soon the new theory of combustion with its satisfactory explanations of the role of air or oxygen in respiration and in calcination began to win acceptance and gradually, but not without much argument and struggle, the older theory was abandoned. Combustion, once thought to be the decomposition of a combustible with the release of its 'phlogiston', was now seen to be a process of chemical combination with oxygen—the oxygen of the air combined with the burning substance. And in respiration it was now seen that the oxygen taken into the lungs was converted into carbon dioxide. In collaboration with the mathematician, Laplace, Lavoisier concluded that respiration was a kind of slow

combustion; and that the constant temperature of the
animal organism was maintained by the heat liberated in
the process of respiration through the combination of oxygen with carbonaceous matter in the blood.

And air was a mixture of two gases, while water was a
compound—neither being an element.

Lavoisier also showed that, in chemical changes, matter
was neither created nor destroyed; the total weight of the
products of a chemical change was equal to the total weight
of the substances originally taken. Chemistry was thus
established on a quantitative basis and the first chemical
balance sheet was now drawn up.

A most important immediate result of these great advances was the reform of the language of chemistry. The
old names of substances had, of course, no relation to their
chemical composition, since that was unknown; and their
chemical composition could not be known until it had been
discovered of what elements they were composed. Accordingly, Lavoisier applied a definition made by Robert Boyle
in 1661 to the effect that an element was a substance that
could not be decomposed into anything simpler; and he
applied this idea in a very cautious way, not asserting that
such substances as appeared to be incapable of further decomposition were, in fact, elements, but that they should
be regarded as elements until evidence to the contrary was
forthcoming. He therefore drew up our first table of chemical elements, which included oxygen, hydrogen and 'azote'
(our modern 'nitrogen'), sulphur, phosphorus and carbon,
and a large number of metals. Further discovery has, of
course, since then greatly increased the number of elements
known to us. Having thus determined what substances were
to be regarded as elements, Lavoisier and some of the
French chemists who had accepted his views set themselves
the further task of devising a suitable system of chemical
names by giving to every known substance a name that
corresponded to its chemical composition. The old names
had often been coined to indicate some physical property
of a substance or its mode of preparation, or to perpetuate
its discoverer's name or the place where it had been found
as a mineral. They were often cumbersome. They were

sometimes nonsensical; for instance, two very poisonous substances, compounds of arsenic and antimony, were known as 'butter of arsenic' and 'butter of antimony'!

The language of a science, Lavoisier insisted, was itself an analytical instrument; the new system of chemical names, which with slight modification is still in use today after more than a century and a half of further discovery, gave us for every substance in a word or two a clear indication of its chemical nature and composition.

The revolution in chemistry was complete and modern chemistry dates from the publication of Lavoisier's great classic, the *Traité élémentaire de Chimie*, published in Paris in 1789, and translated into English and published in Edinburgh in 1790 under the title *Elements of Chemistry*, in which the new system was set out with all the penetrating lucidity characteristic of the French intellect. From this work, which ranks with Newton's *Principia* as one of the greatest of all scientific books, we may quote one sentence that particularly reveals the austere outlook of its author: 'I have imposed upon myself the law of never advancing but from the known to the unknown, of deducing no consequence that is not immediately derived from experiments and observations.'

The new chemistry soon began to yield results. In chemical industry, already beginning its modern development, processes were now better understood and improvements on the old ways followed. Lavoisier himself applied his discoveries in the service of France, carrying out many investigations for the French Government and providing the first example of the scientist in the service of the nation. His earliest important national task was the reform of the manufacture of salt-petre and gun-powder, which he placed on a satisfactory scientific and economic basis; he investigated the principles of ballooning after the first balloon ascents by the Montgolfier brothers in 1783; he helped to draw up the first geological maps of France; he devised a system of lighting cities and large towns at night; and he studied a host of such problems, to all of which chemistry had something important to contribute, for chemistry is the one science that touches our lives at all points.

Science and the scientist are sometimes thought to be concerned only with scientific discovery and not greatly with its application, and still less with the more humane aspects of life. The founder of modern chemistry was one who proved that the finest practice is born of the finest theory; and he showed himself to be a great humanitarian. When the French Government called upon him as the most eminent chemist of his age to draw up reports on the hospitals and prisons, he went much further in his recommendations than dealing with ventilation and cleanliness in the light of the new chemistry; for the hospitals, he urged the classification of patients suffering from different diseases and the segregation of the feeble-minded from the sick; for prisons, he urged the separation of habitual criminals from first offenders and proclaimed his belief that the object of imprisonment was the reform of the prisoner and his return to daily life as a good citizen. His humanitarianism is very evident in his proposals for a state system of education, in which he called education 'a duty that society owes to the child', and for a system of voluntary contributory insurance against ill-health and old age. In the recollection of Lavoisier's reform of the science of chemistry, these other activities are worth recalling. So is his tragic end on the scaffold as a victim of the French Revolution through his former position as an official of the old régime.

X

SCIENTIFIC DEVELOPMENTS
OF THE EARLY
NINETEENTH CENTURY

F. Sherwood Taylor, M.A., PH.D.

Director of the Science Museum, South Kensington

THE early years of the nineteenth century are most significant for the history of science. New facts and theories totally transformed most of the sciences and, quite apart from these, the greatest of all alterations in man's external way of life began when science was applied to industry.

As an example of such a transformation of science we may take the effect of John Dalton's atomic theory (*c.* 1805) upon chemistry. It gave chemistry its modern outlook, its chief aim—the discovery of the connexion of the atomic composition of a compound with its properties. The ideas of the chemists before Dalton's time (with the exception of Lavoisier) seem archaic to us, brilliant as their experimental work may be; but the work of the chemists who followed Dalton—of such a man, let us say, as Berzelius or Liebig—seems sound and sensible; they talk our language, they try to do what we try to do. We shall find, then, in almost every science that the early nineteenth century made discoveries that literally make an epoch, discoveries so fundamental that many years elapsed before their full effect was realised. Yet this was not all. Scientists are not only concerned to discover new facts, to demonstrate new phenomena, and to describe nature ever more accurately:

for they also apply themselves to the utilisation of this knowledge to satisfy human desires. In the years 1800–1850 science revolutionised man's way of life by making available the power that lay hid in coal. There is, of course, always some time-lag between the discovery of a scientific principle and its use to satisfy human needs: and a hundred and fifty years ago, when industry was rarely run by scientists, the lag was very considerable. Thus we shall find that it was principally eighteenth-century science that was utilised by the industry of the early nineteenth century, while the great discoveries of the time bore fruit only in the middle and later years of the nineteenth century. Let us look, then, at what the scientists discovered and the use that was made of it.

First of all, let us consider physics and its applications. One part of that science was well advanced, namely mechanics, to which Newton had given a sound and permanent foundation more than a century before. Thus the men of the eighteenth century had understood the best way of thinking about mechanical matters, namely mathematics: furthermore they had learnt (largely through the making of clocks and scientific instruments) the craft of mechanics, that is to say, the skills needed to form metal into accurate geometrical shapes. Finally the application of the first principles of the science of heat to the crude pumping engines of the mid-eighteenth century had enabled James Watt, after 1780, to produce efficient engines which could turn the wheels and shafts of hundreds of machines. Just before the nineteenth century began the world came to realise the possibilities of the steam-driven machine, and for fifty years after, the story of industry is making, improving and finding uses for steam engines. Steam power was applied to textile machinery in the last two decades of the eighteenth century; in the first decade of the nineteenth century we hear of the first practical steam locomotives and steam boats. The demand for large efficient engines and machines far outstripped the limited skill and power of the blacksmiths and engineers; so in these first decades we hear of a new notion without which industry could never have got far—the use of power-driven machinery to make machines. The eighteenth century depended upon light foot-driven lathes, on files and hammers wielded by strength of arm; but in the early nineteenth these gave place to the newly invented steam-driven power lathes, the planing machines and finally the Nasmyth steam hammer. So great a field was open to this new industry that the greatest part of the country's available resources of capital and labour were deployed in mechanical engineering, first for the textile trade, then in the covering of earth and sea with railways and steamships.

It may be said, then, that one of the great interests of the civilised world was in *power,* and this interest had some further repercussions upon science. The problem of the relation of the 'natural powers'—heat, light, electricity, magnetism, chemical affinity—was always present. The most significant fact about heat was now the fact that it could be turned into work. The newly discovered electric current could also be turned into heat or light or work; it could bring about chemical change (e.g. in electrolysis), and chemical change could result in electricity or in heat or light or work. So we find the men of science gradually establishing the notion that all these 'powers' could be transformed one into another according to a fixed tariff, so to speak, and that they could all be expressed under the single notion of *energy.* It may be thought, then, that the preoccupation of industry with power helped to bring about that great scientific generalisation of the conservation of energy. Yet, in fact, even this connexion between industry and the new science is scarcely a direct one, and it seems that most of the greatest scientific discoveries of the time were independent of industry, or only remotely connected therewith.

Thus we may instance the discovery in 1799 by Volta of the electric battery, which gave for the first time a continuous and comparatively large current of electricity. The scientists of the eighteenth century had been familiar only with the effects of frictional electricity, minute in quantity though of very high voltage. The new discovery led in the early years of the century to the discovery of electrolysis, the electric arc, the electro-magnet and the induction coil, and these in turn led to Faraday's greatest discovery of the possibility of making electricity by moving a conductor in a magnetic field, which was the beginning of the dynamo and electric motor. It led to the establishment of the now familiar notions of electromotive force (or voltage), resistance, and current, and to the laws of electro-magnetism. Yet when we turn to the practical aspects, electricity found no use in industry until about 1840 when the electric telegraph and electro-plating came into use. We may say, indeed, that the electrical discoveries of the period 1800–1835 became fruitful only in the period 1870–1900.

Again, one of the greatest of discoveries in physics, the demonstration that light does not consist simply of streams of little particles, like those of matter, but has the character of a transverse wave-motion, was made in the years 1800–1820; but this discovery scarcely had any effect upon the optical industries until the closing years of the century.

Physics was the most advanced of sciences in 1800; chemistry, on the other hand, though greatly clarified by Lavoisier, consisted of little more than descriptions of compounds and recipes for preparing them. In the years between 1803 and 1808 was made the greatest advance in the history of chemistry—the atomic theory of John Dalton. Atomic theories had been current, off and on, for more than two thousand years, but here for the first time was a theory which proved its worth by making sense of the apparently arbitrary proportions in which chemical elements combined to form compounds. This discovery was perhaps more quickly fruitful for industry than others we have discussed. The atomic theory led at once to the idea of chemical equivalents and formulae; these were the foundation of the theory of chemical analysis, which made possible the scientific control of the chemical industry: furthermore, the light which the theory threw on the relation of one chemical substance to another quickly led to the discovery of bodies that were valuable to man—chloroform may serve as a shining example. Yet the atomic theory, as propounded by Dalton and his contemporaries, was full of difficulties, and it was not until the eighteen-fifties that Cannizzaro persuaded the world to adopt the hypothesis of Avogadro, which made the theory perfectly clear, consistent and applicable to all chemical phenomena. It was, then, indeed that the atomic theory had its triumph, serving in its new form to evolve the wonderful structure of organic chemistry, with its beneficent drugs, beautiful dyes—and destructive explosives. Yet the greatest invention in the chemical industry of the early nineteenth century arose, indeed, from no chemical theories whatever; this was the invention of the process of making and distributing coal-gas. It dates from the opening years of the century, and by 1815 the gasworks were recognisably miniatures of the same type of plant as the gigantic erections that overshadow our cities today; by-products such as ammonium salts were already being extracted, and tar, the source of so many vital chemicals, was being investigated.

Biology was in a far more embryonic condition than either physics or chemistry. The microscope is the biologist's chief tool, and the microscopes of 1800 were not much better than those of a hundred years before. Dollond had invented the achromatic telescope lens in 1758, but no one made an achromatic microscope objective until 1825. That new discovery made it possible to construct high-power microscopes; in 1838–39 Schwann and Schleiden announced the cell-theory of animals and plants—which is perhaps the most fundamental notion of biology. But it was not only the microscope that the biologist needed, for the fundamental activity of living matter is chemical, and the chemistry needed by the biologist was still far in the future. Yet even so, the chemists managed to show that the chemistry of living bodies was, in some respects at least, identical with the chemistry of the laboratory and went far towards exploding the belief in a special 'vital force' that was supposed to build up the constituents of living things.

None the less the chemistry of life remained very obscure and, for that reason, the most conspicuous biological progress was made in the study of the visible characteristics of organisms, and more especially of the extinct organisms of the distant past. Here two lines of research converged. The comparative anatomists, such as Cuvier, studied the laws of structure of living organisms, and the geologists began the study of strata. They found that a particular stratum could commonly be identified by the fossils it contained, and so a tremendous impulse was given to palaeontology, the study of extinct organised beings. This study revealed the past history of the earth, hitherto undreamt of, and forced upon mankind a totally new view of the antiquity of life upon this planet.

These discoveries, though having no result upon industry, were not really unconnected with it. Railway engineering required the first large-scale excavations—cuttings and tunnels. These revealed a great deal of geological information and that information was again useful in the construction of others: thus engineering was at least an occasion of the study of geology, which in its turn led to new knowledge of the past and, in part, to the Theory of Evolution itself.

The biological sciences had little effect upon medicine at this period, the chief advances of which arose from clinical observation or experiment. Jenner's discovery of vaccination was the result of keen observation, not of medical theory. The other great discovery of those times, namely anaesthetics, brought into use in the eighteen-forties, was likewise experimental, though it was the progress of chemistry that made available some of these anaesthetics, such as nitrous oxide and chloroform.

We have seen then, in the years 1800–1840, very great discoveries in most of the sciences, and a gigantic development in the use of power in industry. These had prodigious effects upon man's way of life. Industrial development gathered the workers from the country villages into factories, crowded into cities clustering round the coal and iron on which industry fed. The result in short was to change England from a nation of farm workers and craftsmen to a nation of factory workers dwelling in cities. Nothing was done to ease the transition. Houses went up apace —the worst and cheapest that landlords could let—and almost no regard was paid to sanitation. The resulting incidence of disease was such that it could not be ignored, and the horrible condition of the overcrowded industrial areas stimulated a few men to seek out the causes of this mass of disease and try to prevent it. Such men as Edwin Chadwick and Southwood Smith became convinced of a connexion between dirt and disease, and were the leaders of the movement to procure adequate sanitation. But their progress was very slow, and for two reasons. In the first place no one had proved the connexion between dirt and disease; it was true that those who lived in dirty conditions had a high mortality from what was called 'fever', but 'fever' was also not uncommon among those who lived in the most cleanly manner. To provide adequate sanitation was very expensive, and it could not be done by a stroke of the pen. There was, in fact, the greatest difficulty in getting any alterations made in the systems of sewerage, water supply or housing, because there was little or no legal control over them, and the very idea of controlling any of the apparatus of living was repugnant to the man of the time, who could say with a good deal of truth 'An Englishman's home is his castle', and 'A man may do what he will with his own'. It was only after the germ theory of disease had been proved by Pasteur and others, about the year 1880 that we knew for certain the routes of transmission of diseases, and set ourselves to intercept them.

There is no space to allude to the wonderful advances in communications that resulted from steam transport and their effect in unifying the world; a little reflection will soon enable you to think out the consequences.

Finally, the great success of science convinced men of its importance. Floods of popular books imparted what was called 'useful knowledge' to anyone who could afford a few pence. Lectures on scientific subjects were given all over the country: scientific amateurs set up laboratories in suburban parlours and country rectories. Yet science was very slow to become a regular subject of study in schools and universities. There were some specialist places of instruction, such as the medical schools, in which it was possible to learn a good deal of chemistry. On the Continent the universities had always had many faculties and science was well taught in many cities of France, Sweden and Germany, to which indeed many of our would-be scientists in fact resorted. Our older universities did not consider it their business to train anyone for a profession; they gave the degree of Bachelor of Arts to those who had studied the ancient world through the classics, or to those who had mastered the discipline of mathematics. It was not till after 1850 that Oxford and Cambridge granted degrees in science; the schools followed their lead, and school science-teaching began, in a rather light-hearted fashion, about 1860.

What, then, shall we say of the years 1800–1850? They were the great period of new beginnings in science. The seventeenth century had set out the scientific method, the eighteenth century had established a mass of facts, invented a great variety of techniques and discovered all the mathematics and more that the scientists of the first half of the nineteenth century would need. The early nineteenth century was the age of new beginnings in science, the epoch from which we can date modern physics, chemistry and biology; it was also the time when the use of power began to transform the world. To put it briefly—in those years the civilised world convinced itself of the value of science as a means of explaining the physical world and as a means of getting things done. Not yet did science seem seriously to threaten religion, nor could anyone foresee that by making nations interdependent and bringing them near to each other, science would lead to world-shaking political consequences. All seemed to be well: progress was in the air and the world seemed indeed to be going forward into a roseate dawn of mechanised prosperity and scientific truth.

XI

PASTEUR AND THE
PROBLEMS PRESENTED
BY BACTERIA

Hugh Clegg, F.R.C.P.

Editor of the 'British Medical Journal'

PASTEUR was born in 1822 and died in 1895. His father, a tanner who lived in a town in the Jura mountains, had been a sergeant-major in Napoleon's army. Pasteur lived through the revolution of 1848 and the Franco-Prussian war of 1870. Joseph Meister, the boy from Alsace whom he saved from rabies in 1885, committed suicide when the Germans swept through France in 1940. Pasteur's father had fought under Napoleon. His patient died under Hitler.

Pasteur believed passionately in science. Addressing his beloved France when he was 45 years old he wrote: 'I implore you, take some interest in those sacred dwellings meaningly described as laboratories. . . . There humanity grows greater, better, stronger . . . while humanity's own works are too often those of barbarism, of fanaticism, and destruction.' A man of simple faith, he did not, however, deify science. 'Science,' he said, 'brings man nearer to God.'

As a boy he was quite ordinary at lessons, and when he passed what corresponds to our matriculation his examiners noted that he was only mediocre in chemistry. But Pasteur was not a slacker. Work was his gospel. 'It is necessary to work,' he used to repeat. He had a serious cast of mind and a determination to succeed that we associate more with the

Teutonic than with the Gallic character. In a letter to his prospective father-in-law he said: 'As to the future, unless my tastes should completely change I shall give myself up entirely to chemical research.' In a previous sentence he had written: 'I have absolutely no fortune. My only means are good health, some courage, and my position in the University.' To his future mother-in-law he observed: 'There is nothing in me to attract a young girl's fancy'; and to his fiancée: 'Time will show you that beneath my cold, shy and unpleasing exterior, there is a heart full of affection for you.'

We begin to get a glimpse of the man—serious in purpose, self-dedicated to the pursuit of truth in science, as uncompromising with himself as with others, reserved; perhaps lacking a little in humour, but sustained by a simple piety. Pasteur hated cant and pomposity, and in the controversies at the Academy of Medicine in Paris he was to meet with both. If he fought against these he also had to fight against much personal sorrow and illness. He lost three of his daughters in their youth, and at the age of 46 a clot of blood formed in one of the arteries of his brain, leaving one side of his body paralysed. Yet after he had recovered from this almost fatal illness he made some of his most dramatic contributions to bacteriology.

Pasteur was not a medical man, and it was as a chemist that at the early age of 26 he made his mark as a man of science. He showed that the power of different forms of tartaric acid to rotate polarised light to the left or to the right depended on differences of crystal structure. This was the beginning of what is now known as stereochemistry, and for his discovery the Royal Society of London awarded Pasteur its Rumford medal.

He made three important contributions to solving the problem of bacteria. First, he found that certain microbes—living one-celled organisms—made wine and beer go bad, and that this could be prevented by heating the liquor at a certain stage of its fermentation by yeast. He also proved once more that yeast was a living one-celled microbe—to use a term that includes bacteria and the one-celled animals called protozoa. Secondly, having proved that wine and beer may be infected with microbes, he showed that the same thing can happen in silkworms, cows, sheep, men and women. Thirdly, he discovered that a vaccine made of weakened germs will, if injected into an animal, protect it against subsequent infection by the same germs.

Before we discuss his discoveries in more detail, it may be of interest to look at the work of some of Pasteur's predecessors. The problem of bacteria in relation to disease is the problem of living contagion. That is to say, it is the problem of whether an infectious disease is caused by a living particle, and whether this living particle can be passed on from one person to another by contagion or contact. And if an infectious disease is caused by a living particle, the next problems to solve are the nature and character of the particle, how it lives and multiplies, how it gets about, and what may stop it or kill it.

When Pasteur made his discoveries about the middle of the nineteenth century the idea of a living contagion as a cause of infection was centuries old. So was the idea that infection was caused by a miasma, a sort of gaseous influence in the air. So was the idea of spontaneous generation of life as old as Aristotle, who believed that living eels could be generated out of lifeless mud and moisture. That contagion or contact was a cause of spreading some diseases was understood over two thousand years ago by the Hebrews, who isolated lepers. And the isolation of lepers in leper houses was a common practice in medieval England. In 1546 Fracastoro, who had studied at Padua with Copernicus, suggested that a living contagion was the cause of infection. But the credit for discovering bacteria must really go to van Leeuwenhoek, the Dutch draper, who, at the end of the seventeenth century, saw through a microscope of his own making 'incredibly many, very little animalcules of divers sorts'. The larger ones he thus described and drew were protozoa or one-celled animals. The smallest were the bacteria—one-celled, microscopically small denizens of the vegetable kingdom.

Van Leeuwenhoek did not hit upon the idea that bacteria might cause disease, though he had seen under his

own microscope germs from his own mouth. Some of the
animalcules he described appear in ponds and when hay
rots in water. In the eighteenth century some naturalists
believed that these animalcules arose out of the rotting hay,
and not from father and mother animalcules. They believed
in spontaneous generation. But the eighteenth-century
Italian, Spallanzani, proved by experiment that the animalcules—that is, the protozoa and the bacteria—got into the
infusions from the air. He found that these microbes, as we
may call them for short, were destroyed by heat. He found,
too, that if the air was kept from such a sterilised infusion
no microbes appeared in it. But no one thought of linking
Fracastoro's belief in a living contagion with the invisible
microbes discovered under the microscope and known to be
present in the air and elsewhere. Van Leeuwenhoek, for
example, had described bacteria he obtained from his own
mouth. Fracastoro's theory of a living contagion had to wait
three hundred years before it was generally accepted and
proved. One often sees this sort of thing in the history of
science. A theory, so to say, may remain in solution for
hundreds of years, and then suddenly it crystallises out into
a clear-cut and many-sided structure. This crystallisation
may be brought about by economic forces, by the invention or perfection of techniques and instruments, by the
appearance of the right man and at the right time.

In the 1830's there were three significant developments.
First, great improvements were made in the microscope—
very important. Secondly, French and German scientists
showed that yeast was a living one-celled organism belong-
ing to the vegetable kingdom, and that the fermentation of
sugar into carbon dioxide and alcohol resulted from the
living activity of the yeast cell. It was a live process, not a
dead one. The third was the discovery by the Italian lawyer
Bassi that a certain disease of silkworms was caused by a
certain microbe; the living contagion had been demonstrated. Disease was also attacking silkworms in France, and
the manufacturers were losing money because of it. The
wine industry was being hit economically because so much
wine was spoilt by becoming sour and 'ropy'. There was

much disease among sheep and cows—a serious matter in an agricultural country like France.

These conditions, and certain others, determined the direction and nature of Pasteur's researches. When he was appointed Professor and Dean of the new Faculty of Science at Lille in 1854 he was pompously warned by the Minister of Public Instruction against 'being carried away by his love for science' and urged to 'produce useful and far-reaching results'. But Pasteur did not dwell in an ivory tower. He loved to grapple with practical problems. On one occasion he said of the man of science: 'His cup of joy is full when the result of his observations is put to immediate practical use.' So he was not affronted when a Lille manufacturer asked him to find out what went wrong with the alcohol he was making out of sugar beet. Some months before this, in preparing notes for a lecture, Pasteur had scribbled on a piece of paper: 'What does fermentation consist of? Mysterious character of the phenomenon. A word on lactic acid.' He worked on this problem, on and off, for the next twenty years.

One of his early discoveries was that alcohol was made acid by a living microbe which turned the sugar present into lactic acid—the same acid which makes milk sour. In other words, this was another kind of fermentation, and one that the merchant did not want. Pasteur found that this other kind of fermentation could be prevented by heating the liquor at one stage of its proper fermentation into alcohol—a method of prevention that came to be known as pasteurisation, a term now applied to the heating of milk to make it safe for the consumer. Pasteur's method saved France millions of francs, and has since saved countless lives that would have been lost but for the pasteurisation of milk. He also proved what had been proved before in the 1830's—that the yeast cell was a living microbe which was responsible for the conversion of sugar into alcohol and carbon dioxide. He was not content merely to demonstrate this. He insisted upon it, with zeal and pertinacity. He even bored people about it. It has been said of him that 'Pasteur was not only a savant content to seek the truth and find it, but that when he had in any matter succeeded in the diffi-

cult task of convincing himself he was impelled with almost
a fanatic's zeal to force his conviction on the world.'

While he was working on fermentation, his compatriot,
Pouchet, claimed to have proved the ancient biological
heresy of spontaneous generation. Ardent and indefatiga-
ble, Pasteur entered the lists against him. Finally, in a
public lecture in Paris in 1864, holding up one of his flasks
containing an infusion of hay, he said: 'And I wait, I watch,
I question it, begging it to recommence for me the beautiful spectacle of the first creation. . . . But it is dumb, because I have kept it from the only thing man cannot produce, from the germs which float in the air, from Life, for
Life is a germ and a germ is Life.' Pasteur, as we would say,
knew how to put it across. But in effect he had done little
more than repeat the experiments Spallanzani had made a
hundred years before him.

Describing his experiments designed to disprove the
doctrine of spontaneous generation, Pasteur wrote this:
'What would be most desirable would be to push these
studies far enough to prepare the road for a serious research
into the origin of various diseases.' All this work of his on
microbes in the air, in infusions of hay, on ferments in beer,
in wine, was pointing in this direction. A year after Pasteur's
dramatic exposition at the Sorbonne, Lister, the English
Quaker and surgeon, began to wonder whether these
microbes in the air described by Pasteur caused the horrible
and deadly sepsis of the wounds left after amputation of a
leg or an arm. Lister began investigating bacteria—the one-
celled, living microbes which formed part of that invisible
world progressively made visible in all its variety as the
microscope became more perfect. He became convinced
that the breaking down of his patients' wounds into pus
was caused by infection of them with germs or bacteria
present in the air. Lister attacked the bacteria with carbolic
acid, and thus began the great era of antiseptic or aseptic
surgery. This was a direct—and revolutionary—consequence
of Pasteur's work. Lister, in a letter to him in 1874, told
him of the 'antiseptic system of treatment, which I have
been labouring for the last nine years to bring to perfection';
saying, 'I need hardly add that it would afford me the high-

est gratification to show you how greatly surgery is indebted to you.'

When Lister began his investigations, Pasteur was in the south of France trying to unravel the mystery of a disease of silkworms which was ruining an important industry. He worked for six years on this problem and succeeded in bringing the disease under control. Then in 1868, at the age of 46, he had the stroke which paralysed half his body and nearly killed him. But his gallant spirit rose superior to this disaster, and he lived to make an entirely new and brilliant contribution to the bacteriology of disease. He was asked to investigate a disease, later called anthrax, which was killing the sheep and cows on French farms. The bacteria causing this disease had already been discovered in the blood of diseased sheep in 1850. Pasteur proved that the bacteria discovered did in fact cause the disease. His inquisitive mind then began to work on the idea that the principle behind Jenner's inoculation against smallpox might hold good for other infections. He discovered that he could protect chickens against fowl cholera by injecting them with a mixture of the germs causing the disease—if the germs had previously been weakened in some way. Such a mixture of weakened germs or bacteria is called a vaccine. Then, in 1881, he gave a dramatic demonstration of the effect of a similar vaccine in protecting cows and sheep against anthrax. He injected two batches of animals with a highly poisonous dose of anthrax germs. The animals protected against infection by a previous course of vaccine survived; those cows and sheep which had received no protective vaccine died.

Pasteur then went on to tackle the dread disease rabies, an infection transmitted to man by the bite of a mad dog suffering from hydrophobia. From his experiments he concluded that a human being bitten by a mad dog might be saved if soon after this he was inoculated by gradually increasing doses of the virus causing rabies. In 1885 he successfully put this to the test on Joseph Meister.

All this is but a part of the story of bacteria in relation to disease, and I have said nothing about the good they do. Look, for example, how they rot down a compost heap to fine earth. As Pasteur put it: 'Without them life would become impossible because death would be incomplete.' To sum up briefly. The idea that infectious diseases are caused by a living contagion is centuries old. Bacteria—single living cells—were observed under the microscope in the seventeenth century, and proved in the nineteenth century to be the living contagion which causes many infectious diseases. The approach to this conclusion was through the exhaustive study of two phenomena—fermentation and belief in the spontaneous generation of life. In these studies Pasteur was pre-eminent. Hard work, imagination, and the microscope were his three chief instruments. Not only did he show that microbes cause various diseases in beer, wine, silkworms, hens, cows, sheep and men; he showed how these diseases could be prevented. He was a great man of science and a great son of France. She built in his memory the Pasteur Institute in Paris where men and women still study how bacteria live and die.

XII

THE ORIGIN OF SPECIES

C. F. A. Pantin, SC.D., F.R.S.

Reader in Invertebrate Zoology,
University of Cambridge

My subject in this chapter is Darwin's book, *The Origin of Species*—what it was about and how it came to be written. And also, why it had such an enormous effect on what people thought. For if you could go back a hundred years—about ten years before 'The Origin' was published—most people would have told you that mankind, and for that matter animals and plants too, had suddenly been created a few thousand years ago, and had been as they are ever since; they would tell you the story in the book of Genesis. Today we believe life began hundreds of millions of years ago with extremely simple creatures, which have gradually *evolved* into all the kinds of animals and plants we know today. And we ourselves have evolved in this way from lower animals by way of creatures like the anthropoid apes.

This change in our ideas of how life began was the result of a scientific revolution which followed the publication of Darwin's book in 1859. Like all revolutions, this one had a long history behind it. The public was quite ready for the book when it came. To start with, Darwin did not invent evolution. Even the idea that men are descended from animals is common enough among savage races—a tribe may think they are descended from a boar or a beaver. Men have always speculated about how they came to be here.

I think that our scientific ideas about the matter developed in this way: It was plain, even to the ancients, that animals and plants are of distinct kinds—species. There are dogs; and there are rabbits. You do not find every sort of half-way stage between one kind and another. There are no mermaids between men and fish. The idea that living things could be classed in distinct species was established scientifically in the seventeenth and eighteenth centuries. But even before this was done, philosophers who compared the different kinds of animals noted that they were not just a random collection of every type the mind can imagine. It was possible to place the different species in some kind of order. Dogs and cats are different, but they are related in their structure. They differ from sheep and deer which are themselves related; and so on. The different species seem to fall naturally into well defined groups and classes. That means there is some underlying plan in the relation of the different kinds of animals to one another—and the same is true in plants, too.

Early attempts to explain this underlying plan are often curious. One that goes back to Greek times was the idea of the 'scala naturae'—the ladder of nature. The idea was that not only living things but also inanimate objects could be placed in a continuous series with man at the top. You still see the remains of this idea in the old guessing game 'Animal, Vegetable or Mineral'. The last and most complete scale of this kind was devised by the French naturalist Bonnet. Starting with man at the top, he worked down through the Orang-Utan to apes and quadrupeds. Then came birds, and then fish—with flying fish as a link between the two. Fish, serpents, slugs, shellfish carried you on to worms, polyps and plants. Plants led through toadstools to corals—and that got us safely into the mineral world—by way of asbestos!

Now really, you cannot possibly force all the different kinds of creature into a single scale like that. There are several quite distinct classes of animals. Vertebrate animals are quite distinct from the insects, and both of these differ from molluscs like the snail. All the same, there *is* something to be explained. The great classes of animals do seem to show that there is *some* plan underlying the relation of animals to each other. Some people guessed at a kind of

evolutionary explanation of this plan. When you classify
the species of animals they seem to be related rather in the
same way as members of a human family. We say dogs and
wolves belong to the same family. In human families that
means descent from a common ancestor. Does it mean that,
too, for the species of animals? It might—but it might not.
After all, you can arrange postage stamps in families: letter
stamps, parcel stamps and so on. But just because you can
do this, it does not mean that all the letter stamps were
descended from an aboriginal halfpenny stamp!

About 1800 the evidence of plan in the structure and
relationship of living organisms was often taken to show
that there was some grand design underlying the universe
and its creatures; a design which had nothing to do with
evolution. A parson named Paley developed a very clever
argument. He showed how beautifully the limbs of men
and animals seem designed to meet the purpose for which
they are required. He then pointed out that the same thing
is true of the wheels of a watch—and in that case we take it
as evidence that a watchmaker designed them. Surely, he
argues, design in the bodies of animals means that there
must be—a Grand Designer? It is not surprising that many
held that species were part of an ideal plan of the universe,
and not just the result of evolution. Indeed the men who
first suggested evolution were mostly making wild and un-
scientific guesses.

The first man to make a comprehensive theory of evolution was the Frenchman Lamarck. He tried to derive the
whole variety of living things by descent from simpler forms
of life. Of course, he was quite right about this; but he did
not prove it to be true, and the hypothesis he put forward
was far too complicated. Now there is an important rule
in scientific thought: you must never make more assumptions to explain the facts than are absolutely necessary. Lamarck's hypothesis simply bristled with assumptions. First
of all, he supposed that all living matter had an inner tendency to evolve from the simpler creatures to the more complex ones. But if the simplest animals have always been
striving to become higher ones, we would have to ask—
how is it that there are any simple ones left today? Lamarck

accounted for this by supposing that simple creatures were being made afresh all the time by spontaneous generation from non-living matter. Consequently we had today animals of every grade of organisation. All this by itself would lead to the appearance on the earth of an ideally graded series of creatures, something like the old 'scala naturae'. But Lamarck supposed that the series was broken up because each creature was striving to adapt itself to its special mode of life, and this adaptation was inherited. By striving to reach the leaves on the trees the ancestral giraffe lengthened its neck, and the tendency to develop a long neck became inherited.

Yes, Lamarck's hypothesis certainly bristled with assumptions. Some happened to be right, but many were wrong and unnecessary—like his assumption of spontaneous generation. The extravagance of Lamarck's ideas came in for severe criticism by one of the very best men of science—Charles Lyell. Lyell was then writing his great book on the *Principles of Geology,* the book that began modern geology. Now geologists are very interested in species—you recognise particular kinds of rock by the particular species of fossils you find in them. If Lamarck were right, species were continuously changing—they were evolving. But the work of men like the English naturalist John Ray and the great Swedish naturalist Linnaeus had shown that the whole scientific basis of the classification of animals and plants—living and fossil—depended on the fact that species are surprisingly constant in their characters. If Lamarck wanted to show that in spite of all that, species were really *changing,* it was up to him to prove it. And, as Lyell pointed out, that is just what he did not do.

All the same it was the geologist Lyell who in the end prepared the way for Darwin. For it was he who showed us that, vast as were the changes which must have occurred to land and sea on the surface of the earth, all this could be brought about by natural agencies which we see operating on the earth today—by wind and wave, by glacier and by earthquake—could be brought about, that is, if we allowed enough *time* for their operation. And although Lyell criticised Lamarck, his discoveries made men more ready to think about evolution—about the possibility that we had struggled upwards from lowly forms of life over an immense period, and that man and every creature had not just started suddenly as they are now only a few thousand years ago.

So by 1859 people were interested in, and even excited about, the idea of evolution. All the same it was condemned by the best men of science. It was an idea of the 'wild' men who cheerfully guessed what they did not know. And then came Darwin's book—and in a few years evolution was accepted not only by the enthusiasts but by careful men of science. How did that come about? Let us go back to the beginning. Darwin was born in 1809. At school he was very idle—and he developed his great powers rather late in life. No one nowadays would have given Darwin a scholarship on what he did at school and at Cambridge—in planning education in this country let us remember that, like Darwin, some of the best brains develop very late. But like many children at the time, Darwin was very interested in natural history. So it happened that when, in 1831, Captain Fitzroy of H.M.S. *Beagle* wanted a young naturalist to go round the world with him, it was Darwin he chose.

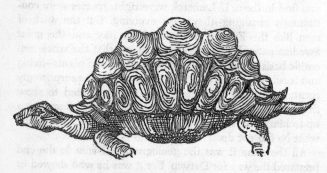

GALAPAGOS TORTOISE

When Darwin set sail he was not predisposed in favour of evolution. But as he travelled round South America the peculiar animals there and the remarkable fossils he found started him thinking about the Origin of Species. Matters seem to have come to a head when he visited the Galapagos

Islands. These islands are 600 miles west of South America in the Pacific Ocean. Among the peculiar animals to be found on them is a huge species of tortoise. After Darwin had been there a little time, one of the officials who lived there happened to point out that you could tell which island any particular tortoise came from by slight but characteristic differences in the shape of the shell. Darwin suddenly saw the significance of this. He soon found that while every island had much the same kinds of plants and animals, each island had its own peculiar and distinctive species and varieties. That struck him as very strange. For *why* should the species have been *created* slightly but distinctly different on each island? Could it be that things did not happen that way? Could it be that the *real* reason was that all the animals and plants were descended from a common stock, and that now they were separated from one another on each island they were *becoming* different? In fact, they were *evolving*? Of course, all this did not prove evolution, but it brought Darwin suddenly up against the fact that an idea that most people treated as a fairy tale had got to be tackled scientifically.

So on his return to England Darwin set himself the tremendous task of trying to prove or disprove the evolution of species. After more than twenty years of patient work he published his conclusions. The plan of *The Origin of Species* is quite unlike that of earlier books on evolution. These were chiefly concerned with circumstantial evidence from the structure and classification of animals which vaguely suggested evolution, but did not prove it. Darwin saw that the key to the answer lay in the study of variation. In his book he starts by discussing variation in domestic animals. Selective breeding of domestic animals was already a highly developed art. Sheep and cattle breeders were constantly improving their breeds by selection—and each man thought he could do it better than his rivals. Here is an old wager between two sheep farmers: 'Mr. Coke will bet £100 to £500 that he produces ten two-shear or three-shear South Down Wethers that shall beat ten of either age of Mr. John Elman's own breed, to be produced at London between the 20th and 30th of May 1798.' Men do not do that sort of thing unless they believe that they know how to improve a breed by selection.

So in his book Darwin reviews the evidence for inherited variations in domestic animals and the way in which selection could give rise to varieties. He then considers variation in nature. He shows that wild animals do vary and that the variation may be inherited.

Then comes an important new argument. A clergyman, Malthus, had shown that in human populations the birth rate was greater than was needed to maintain the number of the people if all the children survived. So the population was always tending to increase. But this increase was held in check by factors like famine and disease. Darwin applied the same argument to living things generally with an important addition. Through rapid breeding, the numbers of a species are always tending to increase. He now introduces the new idea—*natural selection.* Lack of food and other factors limit the numbers that can survive. Only those varieties which are best adapted to the particular environment in which they find themselves will tend to survive in the struggle for existence. In short, Darwin shows that animals vary and that some variation is heritable. He then shows that they breed excessively and that their numbers are continually cut down by adverse circumstance. Finally, he shows that the inevitable result of this must be that the varieties best adapted to meet their environment will survive at the expense of others; and this leads to gradual evolution of species in adaptation to the changing environment. The old arguments for evolution were only based on circumstantial evidence. Each new fact made evolution seem more probable. But the core of Darwin's argument was of a different kind. It did not make evolution more probable—it made it a certainty. Given his facts his conclusion *must* follow: like a proposition in geometry. You do not show that any two sides of a triangle are very *probably* greater than the third. You show they *must* be so. Darwin's argument was a *de*ductive one—whereas an argument based on circumstantial evidence is *in*ductive.

Not all Darwin's ideas had this quality. When he speculated about the *mechanism* of inheritance he was on much less sure ground. It took another sixty years of research to show *how* variation is inherited. After establishing his theory of natural selection Darwin went on in the last part of his book to deal with the circumstantial evidence for evolution which had previously been uppermost in men's minds: the geological succession of animals: their distribution on the surface of the earth: the plan of their classification and many curious facts of comparative anatomy and embryology. All this circumstantial evidence, which first put the idea of evolution into men's minds, was now used much more effectively as corroborative proof of a proposition he had already established.

The conclusiveness of Darwin's argument carried all before it. The old idea that adaptation of animals to their environment was the expression of underlying design in nature was swept away. It now seemed as though the hawk had sharp eyes because it was the sharp-eyed hawks that survived; because dim sight led to extermination through natural selection. There is a very great deal of truth in that; but still it is not quite the whole truth. In recent years the old idea of the underlying plan has begun to emerge again—in a new and very interesting form. Not as in the old days through the study of anatomy, but through the very remarkable properties of atoms and molecules upon which the existence of living matter itself depends. Atoms and molecules did not acquire those properties through natural selection. Why should they have them? It is odd to think that if today old Parson Paley re-wrote his book about design in nature he might have to be, not an anatomist but a biochemist! Whether he would be right or whether he would be wrong would be another matter.

XIII

DARWIN AND

HIS UNIVERSE

Canon C. E. Raven, D.D., F.B.A.

YOU will remember that in the last chapter my friend,
Dr. Pantin, discussed Charles Darwin and his great
book *The Origin of Species*. In that book Darwin explained
his doctrine of evolution. May I remind you of it? (1) All
living things show slight variations—no two members of a
family are exactly alike; (2) these variations are inherited
—John takes after his father; (3) there is a fierce struggle for
existence, so that a very slight variation in strength or cun-
ning or camouflage will give its possessor an advantage and
determine its survival; (4) over the long periods of geological time these successful variations have produced the
vast differences between living plants and animals that we
now know. Darwin called his doctrine Natural Selection;
and collected a vast amount of evidence to prove that Nature was doing slowly what human dog-fanciers did more
quickly—produce totally distinct types.

Two or three times in the history of science there have
come sudden solutions to problems that have been perplex-
ing people for generations. Isaac Newton's discovery of the
law of gravity and Charles Darwin's doctrine of natural
selection each produced an epoch-making change. Each of
them altered man's whole idea of the universe. In each case
men had long been aware that there was a whole realm of
experience waiting to be appreciated and understood; they
had been groping and guessing; and suddenly the key was
found, the doors were opened, and the new realm could be

explored. In Newton's case the effect was to reveal the universe as a scene of ordered law, to suggest that it could be interpreted in terms of mathematics and physics, and so to give an immense impetus to mechanical and afterwards to industrial development. In Darwin's case the consequences were still more revolutionary; for his doctrine dealt not with the laws governing inanimate objects, not with physics and chemistry, but with living creatures, with man and man's position in the scheme of things, and with religion.

Newton's work, as Professor Willey showed in an earlier chapter, did not challenge religion directly. Men had long been realising that God must be a God of order and of law, not arbitrary or self-contradictory; so to think of Him as the Great Mechanic and of the Universe as a perfect piece of machinery did not seem irreligious or even inadequate. Moreover, Newton, like the other great scientists of the seventeenth century, Robert Boyle and John Ray, the naturalist, was a profoundly religious man; and the Christian leaders, great thinkers like Ralph Cudworth and great bishops like Wilkins and Tillotson, were wholly in sympathy with the scientific movement. In any case the scientists were relatively few and their ideas had little popular influence.

With Darwin the position was entirely different. People were already accustomed to the doctrine of *laissez-faire,* the refusal, that is, to interfere with the ruthless competition of 'free' industry, or to allow any measure of social reform. The Chartists and Lord Shaftesbury, Maurice and the Christian Socialists had protested against it in vain. *Laissez-faire* was in fact the doctrine of struggle for existence applied to industry. Darwin's extension of *laissez-faire* as the law of all evolutionary progress was certain of a general hearing. Moreover, since Tom Paine's time, that is, since the French Revolution, the historical value of the book of Genesis and of the stories of miracles and of the Old Testament pictures of God had been very widely challenged. Darwin's new evidence against them was eagerly accepted and employed. So both conservatives and reformers were ready to support him. His doctrine of struggle won the approval of the hard-headed and hard-hearted employers who profited by child-labour and the sweated industries, and his challenge to the literal accuracy of the Bible delighted the opponents of tradition and of prestige.

How, then, were his ideas received by thoughtful Christians? Well, the Christians of the time were in no mood to examine his teaching carefully or to ask themselves how far it really upset their convictions. It is probably true, as Dr. Pantin said in the previous chapter, that most of them still believed that the earth was made in six days and that man was a special creation totally separate from everything else. But there were very many who had long come to feel that the book of Genesis could not be taken literally, and that creation was not a work done once for all, but a continuing and still uncompleted process. Such people were ready, like Charles Kingsley, to welcome Darwin and to say: 'Thank goodness we have at last got rid of the idea that God is a sort of master-magician: we must now choose, if we can, between belief in a world of mere accident and a world which is in the care of an ever-active and indwelling Deity.' Unfortunately (and it is a tragic event, whatever one's views of Darwinism may be), unfortunately the Church leaders as a whole were already scared by the development of biblical criticism and by the growth of liberal theology, and so were quick to feel the danger of Darwin's book as an attack upon their tradition. So they made common cause with the scientists like Richard Owen who had at once denounced Darwinism, and allowed themselves to be represented by the Bishop of Oxford, Samuel Wilberforce, in his violent assault upon *The Origin of Species* at the famous meeting of the British Association at Oxford in the year 1860. There the bishop, a clever and popular speaker but with no first-hand knowledge of the subject, attacked the whole idea of evolution as involving a denial of man's special creation and place in the universe, and concluded by asking Huxley, Darwin's young and enthusiastic supporter who was sitting in front of him, whether he claimed descent from an ape on his father's or his mother's side. Huxley's reply and retort were so crushing as to discredit once for all both the arguments and the taste of the bishop, and to make it appear that in a conflict between eminent representatives of religion and of science the victory was wholly with sci-

ence. It is hardly too much to say that we are still suffering
from the controversy thus begun.

In order to understand the issues at stake it is important
to realise the essential point of controversy. This was not
the matter of Adam and Eve or of the Creation Stories; nor
was it in fact the question of man's ancestry whether from
ape or angel. A more deep-seated conviction was involved
—nothing less than the oldest and most familiar of the arguments for the existence of God, the argument from design.
It seemed to Darwin himself and to many, if not most, of
his readers that he was destroying all belief in there being
any element of purpose in the evolution of life. Now this is
an ancient and universal belief, indeed one of the most
immediate and powerful of all our human reactions to the
world of nature. Let us look at it for a moment.

As soon as men began to reflect and to work upon their
environment—that is as soon as they attained any human
status—they realised that the earth was so constituted that
growth took place in it. There were a thousand difficulties
to be overcome: life, whether human or animal, was always
precarious: but in spite of all the hazards and adventures
living creatures somehow managed to survive. The more
men learnt about the world, about the plants and animals,
about themselves and their needs, the more evident was the
extraordinary intricacy of their existence. It was unthink-
able, even if some philosophers might assert it, that so complex a design could be the result of blind chance, of a
fortuitous coincidence of atoms. If by spilling a million let-
ters at random you could produce a play like *Hamlet,* that
would be a trifle in comparison with the continuous marvel
of an accidental world. So the argument that the design
implies the designer, and that the intelligible order of the
cosmos cannot be explained in terms of a less than intelli-
gent and purposive cause, became the familiar common-
place of all human belief. Cicero formulated it in the century before Christ, but it was an ancient conviction long
before his day. It has always been man's favourite argument for the existence of God; and in the scientific movement, which had so immensely enlarged man's knowledge
of the complexity and the interdependence of every part of

the universe, there had until Darwin seemed to be a plain reinforcement of the truth of that argument.

Now Darwin's contention seemed to destroy the whole idea. Random variations acted upon by the selective influence of the struggle for existence were represented as responsible for all those beautiful and ingenious adaptations of the organism to its environment which John Ray had collected as evidence of 'the Wisdom of God in the Works of Creation'—and which, in spite of Darwin, continue to thrill you and me with a sense of wonder and of awe. Here, then, was no proof of an ever-vigilant master-designer, but merely the operation of a purely automatic process. Here, indeed, was a vast mass of evidence to show that no intrusions of the supernatural, no succession of miraculous acts of creation, need be postulated or could be found in the orderly course of nature. Granted a world like this, its evolution could be explained without recourse to divine interventions and special creations. Scientists could not yet set out the whole course of events from beginning to end. There were still gaps in the record. But it would be unwise for the religious to try to fit God into the gaps.

Now it is, of course, obvious that the old idea of special creative acts, as if every orchid were specially manufactured for its insect, could no longer be accepted. In that sense Darwinism was contradictory of the traditional picture of creation. That is, I think, indisputable. But it is, or ought to be, equally obvious that the real problem is unaffected. It remains as true as ever that the world is so ordered that life develops and the evolution of higher types takes place upon it; and it is as absurd as ever it was to suppose that it is 'merely accidental'. New achievements like the flight of birds, or complex chains of behaviour like the parasitism of the cuckoo, depend upon the simultaneous change of a vast number of factors involving in many cases the creature's whole structure; and the odds against such changes happening all at once by accident are astronomical. Several of Darwin's strongest supporters, like Huxley and Asa Gray, insisted that the belief in an element of purpose in the evolution of life was unaffected. Darwin himself was no philosopher and became on his own confession hopelessly mud-

dled. But for the majority of the combatants on both sides
the issue seemed to be that between a godless and automatic
mechanism and the traditional imagery of Genesis, and with
it the whole Christian religion.

If this was the basic issue raised by *The Origin of Species,*
there were two other points on which it came into sharp
conflict with the outlook of most Christians. The first of
these is as to the place of struggle and destruction in evolution; the second concerns the status and spirit of man.

Darwin himself, though he regarded natural selection as
a chief agent in the evolution of new species, never claimed
that it operated alone, and as he grew older insisted strongly
that he 'had not allowed sufficient weight to the direct action of the environment, i.e. food, climate, and so on'. But
Weismann and the most influential of Darwin's successors
repudiated every other factor except natural selection. In
any case, if elimination played a large part in evolution,
could 'Nature, red in tooth and claw with ravine', be the
appointed agent of a God of love? We can see from Tenny-
son and a multitude of others how violently the pain and
suffering of the animal world shocked the sensibility and
the optimism of the great Victorians.

Similarly, they were convinced that even if Descartes was
wrong in treating all animals as mere automata, he was
quite right in claiming that man alone possessed a soul. God
had breathed into Adam His own breath; separating him
at once thereby from all the rest of His creatures. How
could the lord of creation be descended from an ape? Did
not the whole doctrine of immortality and indeed of the In-
carnation depend upon denying to him so lowly a pedigree?

Now neither of these objections is from the Christian
standpoint as serious as was then supposed. If Christ cruci-
fied is a true symbol of our faith, then it need not surprise
us to find that what Fabre, the great French naturalist,
called 'the sublime law of sacrifice' holds true for all creation. And if God is both Creator and Redeemer, then it is
appropriate that His creation should be 'all of a piece' and
man the end-product of an age-old succession. But here, as
in the first issue, though some few Christians valued the

new knowledge, it was presented in too challenging a shape to escape arousing hostility.

Looking at the whole question now that it has become a matter of history, we can see that at the time Christians might be excused for feeling grave anxiety. That creation was a process, not an act, continuous, not intermittent, operating through the orderly sequence of natural events, upset the whole idea of a God outside the world who set it going, and then on special occasions intervened by miracle to alter its course. We can now see that such an idea was never satisfactory; and in fact it was not the belief of St. Paul or of the first great Christian theologians. But at the time the only alternative to the traditional view seemed to be a purely mechanical and automatic system in which everything could be weighed and measured so that there would be no room for human freedom and responsibility, no sanctions for morality, and no place for religion. Such fears were not in fact groundless. There was in my own young days a period of sheer materialism when it looked as if the scientific and the religious outlooks were wholly contradictory, and when some of us had to say how hard it is to be a Christian not only on moral and spiritual but on intellectual grounds. Indeed, it is still true that we have not yet realised the full consequences of Darwin's work; or seen all its effect upon our traditional ideas.

But this could, I think, be said by way of summary:

(1) The fact of evolution is certain, whatever the precise means involved. Life advances from simple to complex in response to, and in relationship with, its environment. The process of creation is, as St. Paul said in the Epistle to the Romans, still incomplete.

(2) In spite of many set-backs, there is plain evidence of real progress—a travail as St. Paul puts it. Nature and history give the record of fuller and fuller life attained by effort and sacrifice. 'Whoso loveth his life loseth it.'

(3) Religion has gained from Darwinism a new sense of the scale, continuity and significance of the creative process, and a new stress upon the perpetual energy of the living God. If His Spirit shares in the process we can have confidence in its result.

(4) There is room for hope that the goal to which creation moves is the 'manifestation of the sons of God', the emergence of a fellowship or family of free persons, by which His will can be done, as in heaven so on earth.

XIV

THE DEVELOPMENT
OF ELECTRICITY

J. A. Ratcliffe, M.A., O.B.E.

Fellow of Sidney Sussex College, Cambridge

Let us decide, at the start, just what we mean by electricity for the purpose of this chapter. To most people the word suggests two rather different ideas. There is first the electricity of everyday life, the sort that comes into our homes along the mains and that works all the electrical gadgets such as the lamps, radiators, vacuum cleaners, radio sets and so on. Then there is the electricity we meet at school, the electricity of the cat's fur, the electroscope, the tangent galvanometer, the daniel cell, the magnets, the iron filings and all the paraphernalia of the physics laboratory. These two sets of ideas suggested by the word electricity are somewhat different and are worth a little more consideration.

The devices which work from the electric mains are all dependent for their action on a comparatively few important fundamental principles, and although they needed a lot of ingenious development, they don't represent *discoveries* so much as *inventions*. It is useful to distinguish between discoveries, which showed for the first time how some aspect of nature worked, and inventions, which turned those discoveries into appliances useful to mankind. The history of electricity will here mean the history of the discoveries, the history of man's way of thinking about electricity, and we shall not be concerned with the inventions and applications which have turned these discoveries to the use of men.

It is convenient to start our study of the history of these ideas by asking what was known a hundred and fifty years ago. There is a famous text-book written in 1800 by Thomas Young which is meant to cover the whole of science as then known. The first volume of 1,500 pages is devoted to physical subjects, but only about four per cent deals with electricity and magnetism. It is difficult to imagine a present-day text-book of physics in which the subject of electricity forms only four per cent of the whole.

In Young's book electricity is discussed in two separate sections. The first deals with what he calls electricity in equilibrium and the second with electricity in motion. Electricity in equilibrium is what we should now call frictional electricity, and deals with those aspects of electricity which can be demonstrated by rubbing a fountain pen with a piece of flannel so that it will attract bits of paper. When Young writes of electricity in motion he does not mean, as we might expect, the electrical effects which can be obtained with currents produced from batteries, but he is thinking of those effects which were known to be produced when frictional electricity is collected in a condenser or Leyden jar and then discharged to form a spark. He was interested in the heat and the chemical effects which could be produced in this way. The chapter on magnetism deals with the earth's magnetism, magnets and the magnetisation of iron.

Young makes frequent apology for the fact that magnetism and electricity are so little understood, and he makes the most significant statement that 'there is no reason to imagine any immediate connexion between magnetism and electricity'. We shall see that there was not long to wait before a very close connexion had been found.

In the book considerable stress is laid on the novelty of electric and magnetic effects. It is said, for example, that 'the phenomena of electricity are as amusing and popular in their external form as they are intricate and abstruse in their intimate nature', and again of magnetic actions that 'they exhibit to us a number of extremely amusing as well as interesting phenomena'.

Other records agree with Young's book in showing that in 1800 the knowledge of electricity and magnetism consisted mainly of a list of amusing and remarkable experimental facts, but there was little measurement and the scientific meaning of the facts was little understood. The primitive nature of this knowledge and this outlook is remarkable, and even more remarkable are the enormous advances which have been made in the last hundred and fifty years. The lateness, and the rapidity, of the advance in electricity is even more striking when we compare it with advances in the other subjects which are dealt with in this book. Some reasons for it are suggested later.

But first let us survey rapidly the way in which the knowledge of 1800 had been acquired. The ancient Greeks in 300 B.C. knew about a special kind of stone, called a lodestone, which would attract iron, and later it was found that it could be arranged as a compass to point out the north. These stones were the first magnets. Because their behaviour was so unusual they were thought to have all sorts of magical properties, and were even thought to be of use in medicine. The Greeks also knew that amber could be electrified by rubbing, much as nowadays most people know that they can electrify their fountain pens by rubbing them on their sleeves. After the Greeks, during the Dark Ages, little new knowledge was added, and it was not until 1600, when William Gilbert applied proper scientific principles to a survey of the existing knowledge of magnetism and electricity, that any further important advances were made. By this scientific approach he stripped the subject of most of its magical content. He showed that the earth was a huge magnet and explained how the action of the compass followed from that without any need for mystical explanations. In electricity he emphasised that many substances other than amber could be electrified by friction.

After Gilbert's masterly clearing up and ordering of knowledge, progress was still slow and, although some important new facts were discovered, there was no really significant advance till 1785, when Coulomb made the first accurate measurements of the forces between magnets. A little later he also measured the forces between electric charges. He showed that if the distance between two charges is doubled the force will decrease to one-quarter, and if the distance is trebled it will decrease to one-ninth, and in fact, if the distance is multiplied by any quantity, the force decreases to one over the square of that quantity. Now to those who do not know this already it will sound complicated, but the details do not really matter. What does matter is that, for the first time, some proper measurements were made, and the forces were found to behave in the way described. Now forces behaving in this way are said to obey the 'inverse-square law', and this type of behaviour was already well known because Newton had shown just the same kind of behaviour with the gravitational forces which caused the apple to fall to the ground and the earth to go round the sun.

When the first reliable measurements are made in science there is often a rapid advance, and on this occasion the advance was particularly rapid because a very complete theory of forces which obeyed this 'inverse-square law' had been in existence since Newton's time, and soon the theory of electric and magnetic forces was quite fully worked out. This is a good example of the general observation that some of the most fruitful advances in science have occurred when ideas which have grown up slowly in one branch of a subject can be applied, as on this occasion, to another branch.

Here, then, we arrive at the state of knowledge in 1800. Now for the truly remarkable part of the story. This somewhat scanty knowledge developed in a mere fifty years, so that by 1850 the essentials of our present-day knowledge of electricity were known, with two important exceptions which are mentioned later on. Let us first see how the discoveries were made and then try to see why they were made so quickly.

First, in 1800, came Volta's discovery of what we now call the electric battery. He discovered this by following up the fact noticed by Galvani, that if two different metals are put in contact with each other and with the bared nerve of a frog's leg, it is possible to cause a twitch of the leg.

Galvani thought this showed that electricity was produced in the frog, but Volta was able to show that its source was in the contact of different metals with the chemicals in the muscle and, following up this idea, he made an electric battery, by piling alternate discs of copper and zinc on each other, interleaved with pieces of cardboard moistened with salt solution. Other workers immediately started to use these batteries in their own researches. If we remember that there were no proper measurements, it is not surprising that for about twenty years the only useful results from the batteries were of a qualitative nature. The most important of these were in the subject of electrolysis. Sir Humphry Davy was the leader in this line of work, and in 1807 he succeeded in isolating sodium and potassium by passing electricity through molten salts.

Although, as mentioned above, Young thought there was no connexion between electricity and magnetism, people had been searching for a relation between them, and it was natural to start the search afresh with Volta's battery. But since the battery was thought of as a store of frictional electricity, the search was first made by such experiments as suspending the battery like a magnet to see whether it would point north and south, and it took some time for anyone to try whether the *wire connected to the battery* would produce a magnetic effect. In 1820 Oersted showed that it did, and for the first time established a connexion between electricity and magnetism. Now there is much more in this experiment than we might imagine nowadays. For the first time it concentrated attention on the *wire* connected to the battery. As usual, the starting of the new line of thought led to a rush of new discovery. Ampère followed with a wonderful series of experiments by which he was able to demonstrate completely the law of force between small portions of wires carrying current. This involved very difficult ideas, because the forces depend not only on the distances between the wires but also on which way they were pointing.

Apart from these developments of fundamental theory, some important practical inventions followed Oersted's discovery. These included sensitive moving-magnet galvanometers with which for the first time currents could be compared; the construction of electro-magnets and their use to make powerful permanent magnets; and, on Christmas Day, 1821, Faraday's construction of the first primitive form of electric motor.

As a result of Oersted's discovery that an electric current can produce a magnetic effect, it next occurred to several scientists that the reverse ought to happen, and that a magnet could be used to produce a current. Now it is important to realise that there was no real reason for this expectation; it simply was that many investigators who had studied nature closely thought that this was one of those things that ought to happen in a properly constituted universe. In the narrow sense of the words this was a dreadfully non-scientific attitude. Nevertheless there are, fortunately, from time to time, scientists who are so great that, by concentrated study of nature, they almost seem to feel how nature should work, even before they have any proper scientific reason for their belief. Now Faraday was this kind of man, and he was certain that there must be a way in which magnetism could produce an electric current. He persisted in a long series of experiments in a search for this effect and at last, in 1831, he made what is now one of the most famous experiments in electricity and showed how a changing current in one wire can produce a current in a neighbouring wire. This was the discovery of what is now called 'electromagnetic induction'. It was next a comparatively small step to show how to produce an electric current by the movement of a magnet, and from this there emerged a series of inventions leading up to the construction of powerful dynamo-electric generators.

A system of measurement was also required before the subject of electricity could advance rapidly, but among so many new ideas it took some time to come. At first the strength of batteries was described in terms of the number and the size of their plates, and when wires were connected to the terminals their diameter, length and material were always stated. This was the only way of describing what we now call their resistance. In 1826 Ohm introduced the ideas of current, electro-motive-force, and resistance, but it was not till about twenty years later that proper definitions of these quantities were given, and the well-known Ohm's Law was stated in its present-day form.

By 1850 the essentials of our present-day knowledge of electricity were known with two major exceptions. The first of these was the possibility of producing electromagnetic waves, predicted theoretically by Maxwell in 1865 and demonstrated experimentally by Hertz in 1887. This discovery caused a revolution in our theoretical ideas by showing that light was electrical in nature. The discovery also led to the very practical invention of radio communication. The second important discovery was that of the electron, made in 1897. This led to the idea that all matter is electrical in nature, and from it has sprung our knowledge of the constitution of atoms. But this enormous branch of electricity is worth consideration separately, and is dealt with in another chapter.

Now let us look back and ask again, 'Why was the advance in electrical knowledge so slow till 1800 and so rapid afterwards? In what way is electrical science different from the other physical sciences which advanced at a much more even pace, so that comparatively more was known a hundred and fifty years ago?' One reason is that few electrical effects occur naturally, and before men started to make electricity for themselves there was very little to observe. If there were no electric mains or batteries, most people would be unlikely to have encountered any electrical effects, except perhaps lightning and what could be done with a rubbed fountain pen. The facts of heat, sound, light, astronomy or mechanics force themselves on our attention in everyday life, but electricity might remain unnoticed by most people if man had not made it on a large scale. It is not, perhaps, so surprising, after all, that the study of it made such a slow start.

But after the slow start why was the advance so rapid? One reason is that, because the start was late, men's mental equipment was better able to deal with the problems it presented. In particular, there was often a mathematical idea already available for use in the interpretation of a new effect as soon as it was discovered. One has already been mentioned in connexion with the inverse-square law of force.

A second and different reason also arises from the fact that, to show most of the effects of electricity, it is necessary to use man-made apparatus. As soon, therefore, as a new fact was discovered, it could be used to provide a new and better apparatus with which more facts could be discovered, and so on. A process of this kind naturally led to an ever-increasing rate of discovery. It has been pointed out how Volta's battery led to Oersted's discovery of the magnetic effect of a current, which led to the construction of galvanometers with which Faraday discovered electromagnetic induction. This in turn led to the production of electricity on a large scale, which led to further advances and to the discovery that all matter is electrical in nature, as also are the waves of light.

It often seems nowadays that the stage has been reached where no new discovery is possible without elaborate machinery. Let us hope this is not true, and that there may soon arise a new Gilbert or a Faraday, content to study nature with simple apparatus till in the end he comes to *feel* how nature works, and then perhaps to make a fundamental discovery which will open up the way to still further discoveries and inventions.

XV

THE ATOM

Sir Lawrence Bragg, O.B.E., M.C., F.R.S.

*Cavendish Professor of Experimental Physics
in the University of Cambridge*

SCIENTISTS are always talking confidently about atoms and their behaviour, as if they could see exactly what they were like and what they did. At the same time they are very prone to give graphic illustrations of their very small size, such as the well-known one that if a drop of water were magnified to the size of the world, the atoms in it would be about as large as cricket balls. The purpose of this chapter is to give you some idea of the experiments and the reasoning which have led them to their conceptions about atomic structure and atomic properties.

One of the questions which interested the ancient Greeks was 'what is the ultimate structure of matter?' Let us imagine ourselves doing what they pictured, taking a piece of matter and cutting it into smaller pieces, and then each piece into smaller pieces still. Could one go on for ever, or would one in the end arrive at bits which could not be divided any more and were the final bricks of which all matter is built? Democritus suggested that this is so, and called the final bits atoms, or things which could not be cut. He was only speculating, but we can now give his idea a more exact form, and we have adopted his name of 'atom'. We might picture ourselves taking a cube of soap an inch each way, because it would be a convenient thing to cut, and as our first step slicing it into cubes one-tenth of the size each way. Now let us take one of these bits and repeat the process; it would not be very easy, but with a steady hand and a safety razor blade it might be done. Stage three would be a ticklish job; one would have to look at the tiny fragment under a microscope and use what are called micro-manipulators to handle it, but these instruments are now so delicate that even stage four could be achieved with them. Our cubes are, of course, now one ten-thousandth of the size each way of the cube with which we started. The interesting thing is that we are now half-way to the atom. If we could go on, when we reach stage seven we would be chopping into the molecules or little agglomerations of atoms of which soap is made, and at stage eight we would be separating these into individual atoms. To put it more exactly, the distances between the atoms in matter vary from about $1\frac{1}{2}$ to 4 times 10^{-8} cm. or about one hundred-millionth of an inch.

Seeing is believing, and if only we could show these tiny atoms to a sceptical friend under a microscope we should have little difficulty in convincing him that we know what we are talking about. Unfortunately, this is impossible. Light waves are over a thousand times as long as the distances between atoms, and however well a microscope is made it cannot resolve detail finer than the wave-length of light. So we have to rely on circumstantial evidence, as they say in courts of justice. We owe the first convincing evidence for atoms to the famous Englishman, John Dalton, at the beginning of the nineteenth century. He studied the relative weights of elements which combine together to make chemical compounds. He showed that they were always in certain regular proportions characteristic of the various kinds of element, and he explained these proportions by saying that elements were made of atoms, all exactly alike and in particular with the same weight, and that compounds were made of identical molecules, each molecule being a small family of atoms joined together, like, for instance, two atoms of hydrogen and one of oxygen uniting to form a water molecule. Dalton's idea is the foundation of modern chemistry. But the evidence, though it was convincing, was indirect and, of course, it does not tell us what the actual weights of the atoms are, only their proportions to each other.

I cannot enter here into all the discoveries which have made the atom seem so real to us, but I may perhaps describe a few of them which I always regard as exciting ways of reaching out towards an idea of these tiny things which are so much smaller than anything we can hope to see. One of these experiments, which you might try for yourselves, is the camphor movements. Take a bowl of clean water, and with a knife scrape some shavings of camphor, the smaller the better, on to its surface. They dash about in all directions as if they were alive, in a very fascinating way, rather like the beetles one sees sometimes on the surface of a pond. It is what is called a surface tension effect. The pull of the clean water in front of each speck is greater than that of the water in its wake where some camphor has spread, so it is always trying to rush to a cleaner part. Now, any film of grease on the water surface stops the movement at once and 'kills' the particles. Rayleigh had the ingenious idea of measuring the smallest amount of grease which could stop the effect when it spread over the surface. He made a very weak solution of the grease, and counted the number of measured drops which had to be placed on a definite surface. He thus showed that the grease film need only be about one ten-millionth of an inch thick, and guessed that this represents a single layer of grease molecules spread over the water. It was the first estimate of actual molecular size, and we now know that he was right in his rough guess.

There is another effect called 'Brownian Movements'. If one looks at very tiny particles under a high-power microscope, such as the fat globules when a drop of milk has been put in water, or the particles of cigarette smoke in air, they are seen to be dodging about in a random way. You may sometime have tossed a piece of bread on to the surface of a river, and seen it mysteriously jerking and oscillating because many tiny fish, which cannot be seen, are nibbling at it on all sides. The Brownian Movement looks just like that, and the reason is very similar. The particle is being bombarded by the molecules of the gas on all sides. If it is large, the blows average out and it hardly moves at all, but when it is very small it may be hit at a given moment by more molecules on one side than on the other, or by ones which are moving faster; and so it is kept in constant agitation. I always think that this is one of the most convincing demonstrations that a gas is not continuous, but is made up of little particles, the molecules, dashing about in all directions in an irregular way and bouncing off any solid object they touch.

I shall choose my last illustration from the kind of work in which I have been interested during my scientific life, what is called the diffraction of X-rays. One observes very striking diffraction effects when light is scattered by anything which has a regular pattern. You can easily see one for yourselves by looking at a distant street lamp through a stretched handkerchief. The regular pattern of holes between the threads makes a pretty little pattern of coloured spots round the lamp, due to the interference of the light waves after they have passed through the holes. From the size of the pattern and the wave-length of light, one could calculate the spacing of the threads in the handkerchief. Now a crystal is a regular arrangement of atoms. It is not possible to diffract visible light by the crystal pattern, because the light waves are far too coarse, but X-rays are similar to light and ten thousand times shorter in wavelength. When X-rays go through a crystal, a diffraction pattern is formed, and, just as with the handkerchief, one can calculate how the atoms in the crystal are arranged and the distances between them. We can now make drawings or scale models of the arrangement of atoms in many forms of matter, and this has immensely increased our understanding of their properties. These are, of course, just a few examples, but they show the kind of reasoning which makes an atom just as real a thing to the scientist as if he could see it through a microscope or weigh it in a balance.

How are the atoms made up? At first they were thought of as indivisible units, each of its own kind, but you will remember that towards the end of the last century J. J. Thomson discovered the electron. He found that in an electric discharge in a gas little negatively electrified particles could be chipped off, much lighter than an atom, and that these bits were identical whatever atom they came from.

These are the electrons that come from the hot filament in a radio valve, and carry the electric current across empty space in it. Then Rutherford discovered the nucleus, a minute heavy positive speck at the centre of the atom which is holding the negative electrons by electric attraction, just as our sun holds its planets by gravitation. And then, of course, the great problem arose—how does an atom work? How do the nucleus and its electrons make up an atom of oxygen or copper or sulphur, and give to each atom its own particular properties?

I am now going to put to you some real brain-twisters of ideas. Perhaps I am rash to think I am able to talk of such things in this chapter, but I should like to try because, at the least, it may perhaps give you some inkling of the kinds of ideas scientists are trying to develop.

The first attempts were what we might call mechanical models of the atoms. By mechanical, I mean that the bits of the atom were supposed to behave like the parts of some machine which we might imagine ourselves building—in other words, they were supposed to obey Newton's laws of motion like all large-scale bodies do. Now, we are so used to the ideas of energy and velocity and inertia, because everything we observe or do obeys these laws, that it is tremendously difficult for us to conceive of things happening differently. The main point about all these atom models is that none of them worked, and it soon became clear that this was not because the right model had not been discovered, but because no mechanical model could ever be found which would work. Think, for instance, of the electrons whizzing round the nucleus as our earth travels round the sun. They should, in their excursions to and fro, be sending out waves just as they send out radio waves when they dash up and down the antenna at a wireless station. Therefore they are losing energy, and speed, and so finally will all fall into the nucleus, just as the moon would fall into the earth if we could put a brake on it and stop it. There is no escape from this dilemma.

The great Danish physicist, Niels Bohr, was the first to realise that a desperate remedy must be applied to a desperate situation. He said in effect: Let us suppose that, for some reason we do not understand, certain paths or orbits of the electrons around the nucleus are privileged ones. As long as the electron is in one of these paths (whose nature he described) it does not radiate waves. It only does so when it jumps from one to another. He showed that the properties of the atom then fell into a neat and symmetrical scheme and could be explained if, of course, one were willing to accept his dictatorial ruling as to which kinds of orbit were privileged not to pay energy income tax, so to speak. This could only be a half-way house, but it showed where we had all been wrong. In making their models, scientists had in effect said: 'A cricket ball is made of atoms. Atoms are made of bits, and these bits behave like tiny cricket balls.' It is quite illogical, a complete arguing in a circle. Why should the bits behave like the whole? We must give up some of our ideas gained from looking at large-scale things.

This may seem natural enough, though it was hard to realise at first, but when I indicate one of the main ideas we had to give up, you will see how very revolutionary we have to be. We must abandon the idea that a thing can only be in one place at one time. Before you think what a nonsensical idea this is, be patient while I try to explain.

Our difficulty is that of understanding how the electron goes round the nucleus without sending out waves, when it is in one of Niels Bohr's privileged orbits. What do we mean by 'going round'? Why, that if we looked at it we would see it first at one end of the atom and then at the other. But it could only be seen if it were emitting waves, and we have just said that it is not emitting waves. Therefore, as by definition it has no possible way of telling the outside world that it is first at one end of the atom and then at the other, there is no sense in supposing it is in any one place more than another. In fact, it is all round the atom simultaneously, the only possible thing it can be if it is to remain unobserved. When we make an experiment and 'see the electron', it is a little particle in a place. When it is unseen, saying it is in a place has no meaning. This argument may sound like hair-splitting, or airy philosophising, but the point is that it delivers the goods. If put into a mathematical form, the properties of the atom can be calculated, and they all turn out to check with experiment in the most delightfully pleasant way.

Let me try to explain what I mean by an analogy. Sometimes at an annual prize-giving a headmaster has been known to say that there is 'a good spirit in the school'. Where is the good spirit? At the east end of the school or the west end? Does he keep it in a matchbox in his study? While the spirit is just existing, not making itself manifest, it is of course in no particular place. But when it shows itself, it momentarily is in a place, being displayed perhaps by Jones minor being a sporting loser, or a prefect handling a difficult situation cleverly. We have got to think about the electrons in the atoms in just this way. As long as they are just existing in the atom and not sending out waves, they cannot be thought of as little localised particles travelling about; they are just something all over the atom at once. You may object that we are talking about material things, not spirits, and that a thing like a cricket ball has a completely definite place at any given time. But we only get this idea of it because a cricket ball is a large thing made up of many elements. If you gave the headmaster a map of England and asked him where the good spirit was, he would very definitely stick a pin in the town in which his own school was, and be positive that it wasn't in the school in the next town. It is just the same with our electron. As we approach the scale of the atom, the idea of 'being in a place' becomes more and more fuzzy, a kind of vague probability, and finally is seen to have no meaning at all, unless of course the particle manifests itself by sending a message to the outside world, when we can at once say where it was at that moment.

Science used to be called Natural Philosophy, and it was a very good name. The fun in science lies not in discovering facts, but in discovering new ways of thinking about them. The test which we apply to these ideas is this—do they enable us to fit the facts to each other, and see that more and more of them can be explained by fewer and fewer fundamental laws? This better understanding of the nature of the atom has been one of the great triumphs of the last generation. I hope I have given you at any rate some idea of the exciting voyaging through strange seas of thought which has led to it.

XVI

SCIENCE TODAY

M. L. Oliphant, F.R.S.

*Formerly Poynting Professor
in the University of Birmingham*

THE natural curiosity of man has produced the material civilisation which we know and has added immeasurably to the storehouse of our knowledge. It has contributed greatly to that subtle measure of the maturity of nations which, for want of a better term, we call 'culture'. In short, this inborn curiosity is the principal factor which has made for progress. In modern times this desire for knowledge is expressed most forcibly in our pursuit of science. The exploration of the geographical world is now almost complete, but the spirit of Drake and Cook lives on in those who explore the inside of atoms or the complicated molecules from which living things are made.

In earlier chapters of this book the different branches of scientific thought and experiment have been discussed. You have seen that a study of past achievements shows how these have led to revolutionary changes in thinking and behaviour. The pace of scientific advance is now so great, and is accepted with so little question, that we are in danger of overlooking its effect upon ourselves, and hence may not appreciate where it is leading us. It is my purpose to say what I believe is happening to us as a result of our increasing knowledge of nature.

In what follows I shall try to show how ignorant most men are of the simple facts of science, yet how great is the influence on their everyday lives of the continuing advance of scientific knowledge. As a result the future of the majority of men, their present social and political outlook, and the actions they take, are being determined by facts completely outside their own control. This situation is very dangerous and it is one of our tasks for the future to help rectify it by making all people more fully aware of what is happening, and why. You will see that, in my view, one answer to the difficulties created by scientific advance is, strangely enough, a more widespread knowledge of science, and greater speed in its application for the welfare of all mankind. Then I shall indicate how strongly our minds are influenced by the philosophical implications of scientific advance, and how changes of outlook more revolutionary than any in the past are taking place today. Lastly, I shall state my belief that science, if not misused, is the greatest power wielded by man for the promotion of international peace and understanding.

At first sight modern science seems to be an immensely complicated mixture of fact and fancy. Carefully observed and corroborated facts, the results of experiments made with great precision and the pictures of the way nature works which this mass of data reveals, are found side by side with almost as large a volume of speculation. Theoretical calculations about the interior of stars, unprovable hypotheses about the existence of neutrinos in physics or of enzyme systems in chemistry, guesses about animal behaviour, and so on, present so bewildering a picture that the non-scientist finds it difficult to know what to believe. Yet this boiling-up of hypotheses from the cold facts is the very spirit of science, for a guess suggests experiments to prove it, and so the truth is slowly sorted out. Speculations which stretch out beyond existing knowledge are exciting and exhilarating, and so long as we do not take them too seriously, or believe them as fact, provide one of the best examples of the working of the human intellect. It is a duty of science to make these guesses, and it is equally a duty to test them in every way possible by experiment and observation, rejecting ruthlessly those which prove false or incomplete. The difficulties experienced by ordinary men and women in understanding how science works arise largely from the use of the most terrible jargon and of unnecessary technical terms, and from the complexities of scientific proof.

Actually, what we really *understand* is extremely simple. For instance, a 'facial cutaneous vasodilation' is just an ordinary blush, 'crystalline hydrated sodium carbonate' is washing soda, 'non-relativistic two-dimensional space' is the ordinary flat surface on which we draw our diagrams in geometry. Similarly, while the evidence from which we infer where atoms of chlorine and sodium in a crystal of common salt are located is complicated and full of technicalities, the fact that the atoms sit at the corners of cubes is simple and satisfying.

The proven facts of science are soon woven into the fabric of our lives. They appear in the text-books we use at school and the universities. The mathematical relationships between measured quantities, which seemed so exciting when first discovered, become exercises and examples in applied mathematics. Scientists working in industry use these facts to work out new processes and give us new products, new trades, new varieties of plants, more useful breeds of animals or fresh ways of amusing ourselves. They are soon accepted as part of the background of modern living.

It is difficult for us to believe that such facts as the rotation of the earth round the sun or the atomic nature of matter are comparatively recent discoveries of man. We cannot imagine a world without electricity, yet it is scarcely a hundred years since Faraday, in his search for a connexion between electricity and magnetism, made the discoveries which were the foundation of electrical engineering. Sixty years ago we knew nothing of electrons or of radioactivity, yet from the discoveries made at the turn of the century by J. J. Thomson, Roentgen, Becquerel, the Curies and Rutherford, have emerged radio broadcasting and television, all our knowledge about atomic structure, and atomic energy. The work of Gowland Hopkins on 'accessory food factors' has stocked the chemists' shops with vitamins. Ten years ago penicillin was a remarkable curiosity discovered by Fleming, but through the magnificent work of Florey it is now available to cure all who need it.

We see that as we become familiar with new facts about nature we soon accept them without question. We store them away in books and periodicals and in the minds of a very few individuals. At the same time we rely more and more, in our daily lives, on the material products which they make available. Men are divided rather sharply into three groups in their reaction to science—those who are avid for new knowledge and who absorb all they can under-stand; those who see science in the service of man, in-creasing his ability to mould the world to serve mankind; and those who, though completely indifferent to science itself, are deeply influenced by the effect it has on their lives. The first group includes not only the professional scientist, but the amateur with deep interest in natural his-tory, astronomy, or radio; the men and women who were thrilled by Fred Hoyle's talks on the Third Programme, and those who read the popular books on science. The second consists of those who recognise that the results of scientific investigation provide the basic knowledge on which to build new inventions for use in industry and com-merce. The third, unhappily the majority of men, is only indirectly and often unconsciously influenced by the ad-vance of knowledge, and does not realise that the world in which it lives is undergoing a continuous and accelerating transformation as a result of the applications of science.

I do not think it is necessary for me to say much about the real scientists. In the fundamental sciences the driving force comes from the excitement of the chase, the grand intellectual thrill which comes from participation in new discoveries and fresh hypotheses. In the applied sciences also the inspiration is the fun of engaging in the develop-ment of new things and processes, though here the more objective goal of contributing to industry limits the field over which a given scientist may wander. The majority of men are as uninterested in the workings of nature in gen-eral as they are in the processes taking place in their own bodies. For many there is something indecent and un-natural in trying to understand the world in which they live. For these the glories of a sunset fade before an ex-planation of how these gay colours are produced; a description of the wonderful growth of a baby from the fertilised egg is something horrible, to be thrust away and kept from contemplation like thoughts of death. Yet these same individuals accept without question the fruits of scientific advance—new drugs to cure their ills; improved modes of transport on sea and land and in the air; foods preserved by modern methods; fluorescent lighting; the radio and television, and so on. After a gasp of horror they accept in the same way the domination of the world by the less desirable fruits of science, like bacteriological and chemical warfare, atomic bombs of increasing destructive power, or the decreasing fertility of the earth produced by greedy exploitation of its wealth. This strange indifference to the forces moulding all our lives, arising from the growth of knowledge, is due, possibly, to lack of education in science during the years of schooling of so great a part of mankind, but it is primarily another manifestation of that mental laziness which substitutes pictures for reading, football pools for thinking, and watching games for taking part in them.

Now in a world where people react to science in the three ways I have described, what is the situation we find? Well, no nation can achieve the first rank today without a most elaborate system whereby science is applied intensively to all problems of defence, industry and health. Indeed, the power once wielded by individuals who inherited command over states and armies has given place completely to power based on the exploitation of science. It is one of the tragedies of our day that science, which has so increased the intellectual stature of man and is such a power for good, should be directed to the development of weapons for the wholesale destruction of man. Modern methods of communication and transport, arising in particular from the very great scientific effort devoted to aircraft design and radio, have made war between major nations inevitably become total war involving the whole world.

The total sum devoted to scientific investigation and development for purposes of war is greater in the United Kingdom than the sum spent on research of all other kinds.

This effort is not all wasted, for many of its results, such as jet engines for aircraft, can be used for peaceful purposes, and much knowledge of general applicability is obtained. However, it does mean that the scale of such important research as that in the field of medicine is trivial in comparison. In the modern state we no longer keep standing armies of great size, but we spend as much or more on preparations for war on a global scale. This is one example of the revolution in our outlook and actions brought about by advance in scientific knowledge.

The tremendous power of technology, based on pure and applied science, is evident to all. Absolute dictatorships on the scale of those of Hitler and Mussolini, or group dictatorship from the centre, as practised in Russia today, would be impossible without the telegraph, telephone, radio and modern weapons to enforce obedience.

At election times we pretend that the domestic issues are within our own control, but under modern conditions we are influenced in all we do by what other nations think and do. The very existence of the United Nations is a recognition of the fact that all politics are now world politics. Our own precarious financial and economic position is due more to what is happening outside Britain than to our own actions or lack of action. It is recognised that our one hope of succour is by applying science to our industry and our economy in general more intensely and with more intelligence than happens in other countries.

America is afraid of Russia, and Russia of America, because scientific developments have made it possible for nations in opposite hemispheres of the earth to influence one another profoundly and to fight across the seas. The whole tense atmosphere which we experience on a world-wide scale is due to the rapid advance of science and technology.

No historical event of the past has influenced the world and the lives of men as has the rapid progress of science in the last century. The effects of the great military campaigns of history, the rise of the great empires of the past, the revolutionary changes of outlook produced by the great religions of the world—all these were far less important than the modern revolution, the unification of the world, brought about by scientific advance. We are living in the midst of changes more far-reaching than anything which has ever happened before.

While these material changes are taking place and producing profound effects on the minds of men, the advance of fundamental knowledge is changing our philosophy. Observations of the depths of space with huge telescopes show that, the further we see, the more galaxies of stars become apparent. This limitlessness of space suggests an infinite universe expanding outwards towards still greater infinity of distance. At the same time increasing knowledge of atoms and their nuclei has given rise to new kinds of mechanics based on probability rather than on certainty that a given effect follows a definite cause. The known laws of physics do not apply inside the nucleus, and physicists are groping after new conceptions to explain the behaviour of the infinitely small. New knowledge about the patterns in which the atoms which compose proteins are arranged brings us closer to the fundamental problem of the difference between living matter, all of which contains proteins, and inanimate matter. The effect of trivial biological changes brought about by surgical interference or drugs on the personality of animals and men focuses attention upon the whole meaning of individuality. All these things have a profound influence on our mental appreciation of the world around us and hence make it necessary to re-think the philosophy of our time. They give rise to controversy which is amusing to the scientist, who is very conscious that his knowledge is as yet very rudimentary, so that the very basis of today's argument may have disappeared by tomorrow. So much for the present situation. In conclusion, let us look ahead. What revolutionary changes may we reasonably foresee?

Advances in medical science increase continually the expectation of life of every child which is born. The length of life of men and women has been increased so that older people form an increasing proportion of our population. Perhaps this means that more of us will pass through the frantic days of youth and fruitful middle age to a more contemplative old age. This may lead to a growing maturity of outlook, devoid of crusty conservatism because of the greater vigour of older people, yet with wisdom gained from experience of life. While the young continue to produce the new ideas and the driving force of our economy, the riper judgment of the older citizens may give us better relations with one another inside and outside our own nation. Already there is a growing realisation that the good which science can do in health, economics and general outlook belongs to all, to the under-developed nations as to us. The spread of medicine, scientific agriculture and industry into the countries of the East has become a duty to mankind and not a way of exploiting others for our benefit. The solution of the greatest problem facing us, that of sharing the world and its products between the coloured and the white races, is more likely to come from the spread of medical and scientific knowledge than from the efforts of politicians. Science, unless subject to gross political interference, knows no boundaries of race, nation or creed. Its language is international and its principles are accepted by all who work in its fields. When it is not misused for political ends or to further personal ambitions, it is the greatest power for peace and international understanding in the world today.

These things of which I have spoken, and many more, have changed completely our intellectual approach to the world around us. The stature of man has increased greatly under the influence of our advancing knowledge, and science is emerging as the greatest cultural influence of all time.

BIBLIOGRAPHY

This bibliography gives, in most cases, the date of the most recent American edition. No attempt has been made to indicate which books are out of print because the bibliography, as well as indicating what books may at present be bought new, is intended as a guide to library borrowing or secondhand buying. Numbered books are referred to in the suggestions for further reading. Starred books are only suggested for those who wish to make a more detailed study of the subject of a particular chapter.

GENERAL HISTORIES

Butterfield, H., *Origins of Modern Science*. Macmillan, 1941.

Singer, C., *A Short History of Science*. Oxford, 1941.

Taylor, F. S., *Science Past and Present*. London: Heinemann, 1949.

Taylor, F. S., *A Short History of Science*. Macmillan, 1939.

MORE DETAILED BOOKS USEFUL FOR REFERENCE

Lenard, P., *Great Men of Science: A History of Scientific Progress*. London: Bell, 1933.

1. Lilley, S., *Men, Machines, and History*. London: Cobbett Press, 1948.

Pledge, H. T., *Science Since 1500*. Philosophical Library, 1947.

2. Usher, A. P., *A History of Mechanical Inventions*. Harvard University Press, 1954.

Westaway, F. W., *The Endless Quest: Three Thousand Years of Science*. London: Blackie, 1934.

Whetham, W. C. Dampier (later Dampier, W. C.), A

History of Science and Its Relations with Philosophy and Religion. Macmillan, 1932.

3. Wolf, A., *A History of Science, Technology, and Philosophy in the Sixteenth and Seventeenth Centuries.* Macmillan, 1951.

4. Wolf, A., *A History of Science, Technology, and Philosophy in the Eighteenth Century.* Macmillan, 1952.

PHILOSOPHY AND SCIENCE

5. Conant, J. B., *On Understanding Science.* New American Library, 1952.

   Dingle, H., *Through Science to Philosophy.* Oxford, 1937.

6. Eddington, Sir A. S., *The Nature of the Physical World.* Cambridge, 1932.

   Ritchie, A. D., *Scientific Method.* Harcourt Brace, 1923.

   Russell, B., *Religion and Science.* Oxford, 1935.

   Singer, C., *Religion and Science.* J. Cape & H. Smith, 1929.

   Taylor, F. S., *Concerning Science.* Macmillan, 1949.

   Whitehead, A. N., *Science and the Modern World.* New American Library, 1948.

SCIENCE BEFORE DANTE

Haskins, C. H., *Studies in the History of Medical Science.* Harvard University Press, 1924.

Read, J., *Prelude to Chemistry.* London: Bell, 1936.

7. * Sarton, G., *Introduction to the History of Science.* Williams and Wilkins, Vols. 1 & 2, revised edition, 1950; Vol. 3, 1948.

   * Thorndike, L., *History of Magic and Experimental Science during the First Thirteen Centuries of Our Era.* Columbia University Press, 8 vols., 1923–50.

PARTICULAR SCIENCES

Bell, W. W. R., *A Short Account of the History of Mathematics.* London: Macmillan, 1888, 1924.

Buckley, H., *A Short History of Physics.* London: Methuen, 1927.

Cajori, F., *A History of Physics in Its Elementary Branches*. London: Macmillan, 1899.

Einstein, A., and Infeld, L., *The Evolution of Physics*. Simon & Schuster, 1938.

Jeans, Sir J., *The Growth of Physical Science*. Cambridge, 1951.

Partington, J. R., *A Short History of Chemistry*. St. Martin's Press, 1948.

Raven, C. E., *English Naturalists from Neckham to Ray*. Cambridge, 1947.

8. Singer, C., *A Short History of Biology*. Abelard Schuman, 1950.

9. Singer, C., *A Short History of Medicine*. London: Oxford, 1928.

(See also *The Early History of Science: A Short Handlist*. London: The Historical Association: George Philip & Son, 1950.)

SUGGESTIONS FOR FURTHER READING

CHAPTER I

Bibliography No. 7.

Dante, *Convivio*. London: Temple Classics, Dent.

Gilson, E., *La Philosophie au Moyen Age.** Paris, 1944.

Orr, M. A., *Dante and the Early Astronomers*. London: Gall & Inglis, 1914.

Duhem, P., *Le Système du Monde.** Paris: Hermann, 5 vols., 1913–17.

(Useful both for this chapter and the two which follow.)

CHAPTER II

Bibliography Nos. 1, 2, and 7.

Pirenne, H., *History of Europe,** trans. B. Miall. Doubleday Anchor Books, 1958.

CHAPTER III

Armitage, A., *Copernicus: Founder of Modern Astronomy*. T. Yoseloff, 1947. *Sun Stand Thou Still: The Life and*

Work of Copernicus the Astronomer. Abelard Schuman, 1947.

Dingle, H., "The Work of Copernicus," in *Polish Science and Learning,* June 1945.

CHAPTER IV

Bacon, F., *The Advancement of Learning* (1605); various standard editions. *Novum Organum* (1620). P. F. Collier and Son, 1901.

Broad, C. D., *The Philosophy of Francis Bacon.* Macmillan, 1926.

CHAPTER V

Bibliography No. 9

CHAPTER VI

Bibliography Nos. 1, 2, 3 (chapters 5, 8, 11), 4 and 5.

CHAPTER VII

Bibliography No. 6.

Clark, G. N., *Science and Social Welfare in the Age of Newton.* Oxford, 1949.

Duhem, P., *The Aim and Structure of Physical Theory,* trans. Philip Wiener. Princeton University Press, 1954.

Hazard, P., *European Thought in the Eighteenth Century.* Yale University Press, 1954.

Snow, A. J., *Matter and Gravity in Newton's Physical Philosophy.* Oxford, 1926.

CHAPTER VIII

Bush, D., *English Literature in the Early Seventeenth Century, 1600–1660.* Oxford, 1945.

Tillyard, E. M. W., *The Elizabethan World Picture.* Macmillan, 1944.

Willey, B., *The Seventeenth-Century Background.* Doubleday Anchor Books, 1953.

Willey, B., *The Eighteenth-Century Background.* Columbia University Press, 1941.

CHAPTER IX

McKie, D., *Antoine Lavoisier*. H. Schuman, 1952.

CHAPTER X

Simon, Sir J., *English Sanitary Institutions*. London: Cassell, 1890; Smith Elder (now Murray), 2nd edition, 1897.

Taylor, F. S., *A Century of Science*. London: Heinemann, 1941.

CHAPTER XI

Compton, P., *The Genius of Louis Pasteur*. London: Alexander Ouseley, 1932.

CHAPTER XII

Bibliography No. 8.

CHAPTER XIII

Raven, C. E., *Science, Religion and the Future*. Macmillan, 1943.

CHAPTER XIV

Crowther, J. G., *Famous American Men of Science*. W. W. Norton, 1937.

Thompson, S. P., *Michael Faraday: His Life and Work*. Macmillan, 1898.

CHAPTER XV

Andrade, E. N. da C., *The Atom and Its Energy*. London: Bell, 1947. *Science News No. 2* (Atomic Energy Number). London: Penguin Books, 1947.

Gamow, G., *Mr. Tompkins in Wonderland*. Cambridge, 1939. *Mr. Tompkins Explores the Atom*. Cambridge, 1945.

ANCHOR BOOKS